BLOCKBUSTERS QUIZ BOOK 4

This book adaptation of *Blockbusters*, the very successful Central television series game, can be used in one of two ways. By yourself you can solve the clues as you would a crossword puzzle, writing the answers in the spaces provided and shading or colouring in the hexagons; or, you can play it as a game with friends, one being the quizmaster and two being competitors, one trying to get a linking pattern of hexagons across and one down.

Whether you solve the clues yourself, or with friends, you'll have hours of amusement and have masses of information at your fingertips.

Also in the Blockbusters series in Sphere Books:

BLOCKBUSTERS QUIZ BOOK 1
BLOCKBUSTERS QUIZ BOOK 2
BLOCKBUSTERS QUIZ BOOK 3
BLOCKBUSTERS GOLD RUN

Blockbusters
Quiz Book 4

Based on the Central Independent Television series produced in association with Mark Goodson and Talbot Television Ltd

SPHERE BOOKS LIMITED

First published in Great Britain by
Sphere Books Ltd 1986
27 Wrights Lane, London W8 5TZ
Reprinted 1986
Copyright © 1986 by Sphere Books Ltd
Central logo copyright © 1982
Central Independent Television plc.
Central Television programmes © 1983, 1984, 1985, 1986
Central Independent Television plc.

Blockbusters Quiz Book 4 compiled by Bill Garnett

Sphere Books claim full responsibility for the questions
and answers in this volume and every effort has been made to
ensure their accuracy.

TRADE
MARK

Set in Times

Printed and bound in Great Britain by
Cox & Wyman Ltd, Reading

Blockbusters
Quiz Book 4

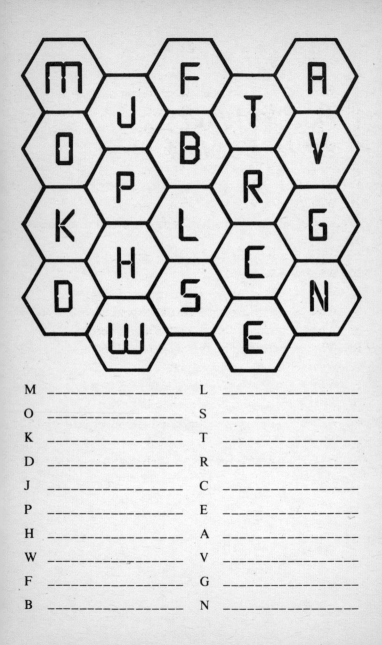

M _____   L _____

O _____   S _____

K _____   T _____

D _____   R _____

J _____   C _____

P _____   E _____

H _____   A _____

W _____   V _____

F _____   G _____

B _____   N _____

1

M: What 'M' is an old Scots word for much?

O: What 'O' means dim or indistinct?

K: What 'K' is a South African enclosure for animals?

D: What 'D' is compulsion?

J: What 'J' is a unit of work or energy?

P: What 'P' is pastry, an adder – and a ball?

H: What 'H' is a wrangle or trying problem?

W: What 'W' is the Norse god a day of the week is named after?

F: What 'F' are the Europeans who call themselves *Suomi*?

B: What 'B' is hairless?

L: What 'L' is a substance to minimise friction?

S: What 'S' is a long-winged, fork-tailed insectivorous bird?

T: What 'T' comes before bug, down and weed?

R: What 'R' means to repent or deeply regret?

C: What 'C' is a metal container?

E: What 'E' is a major British public school?

A: What 'A' is a nautical term meaning stop?

V: What 'V' is an organic compound essential to nutrition?

G: What 'G' is a picturesque cave?

N: What 'N' comes before Front, Velvet and anthem?

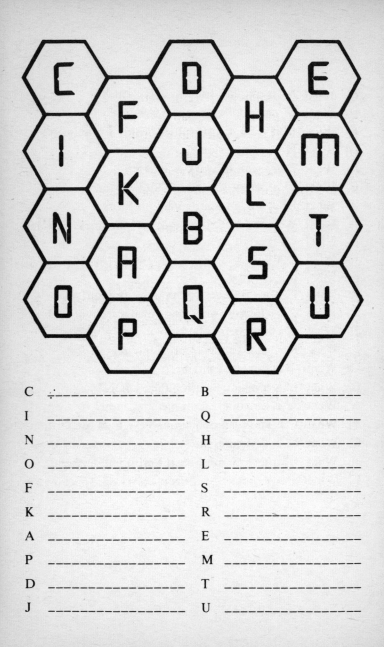

C _____   B _____
I _____   Q _____
N _____   H _____
O _____   L _____
F _____   S _____
K _____   R _____
A _____   E _____
P _____   M _____
D _____   T _____
J _____   U _____

C: What 'C' means attractive or pretty?

I: What 'I' is a close examination?

N: What 'N' is the largest British bat?

O: What 'O' is a group of eight singers or players?

F: What 'F' means full of fury?

K: What 'K' do Eskimos do by rubbing noses?

A: What 'A' means friendly?

P: What 'P' is a chicken less than one year old?

D: What 'D' comes before bin, jacket and pan?

J: What 'J' is to talk or gossip for a long time?

B: What 'B' is one meant to be as blind as?

Q: What 'Q' is a hard, yellow, acid fruit rather like an apple?

H: What 'H' is to visit or inhabit as a ghost?

L: What 'L' is a song to send you to sleep?

S: What 'S' is a fruit drink, tight mass of people – and ball game?

R: What 'R' founded the Singapore colony and London Zoo?

E: What 'E' means to praise or place high in rank?

M: What 'M' is a British duck?

T: What 'T' originally meant great prince in Japanese?

U: What 'U' is an indentifying dress worn by members of the same group?

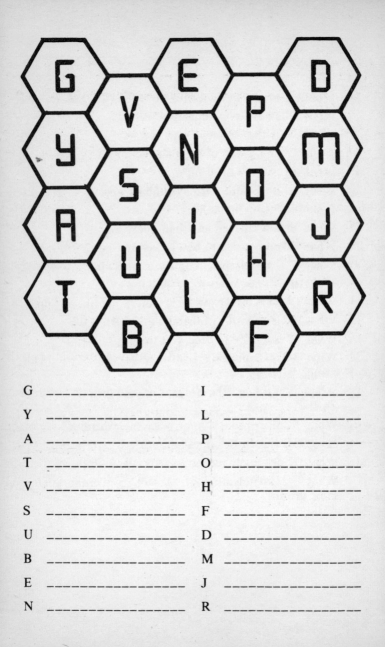

G _____ I _____

Y _____ L _____

A _____ P _____

T _____ O _____

V _____ H _____

S _____ F _____

U _____ D _____

B _____ M _____

E _____ J _____

N _____ R _____

G: What 'G' is a morbid enlargement of the thyroid gland?

Y: What 'Y' is the Christmas festival?

A: What 'A' lies north and west of Pakistan?

T: What 'T' was an English landscape painter?

V: What 'V' are all plants?

S: What 'S' means to show off or swagger?

U: What 'U' is all things that exist?

B: What 'B' invented Tarzan?

E: What 'E' comes before witness, lash and tooth?

N: What 'N' is a wally?

I: What 'I' means to make poor?

L: What 'L' is a type of beer?

P: What 'P' is the rubber disk used in ice hockey?

O: What 'O' is spoken?

H: What 'H' is slang for advertising or promotion?

F: What 'F' means untrue?

D: What 'D' is double-dealing?

M: What 'M' is largeness or importance?

J: What 'J' is US slang for loo?

R: What 'R' are the beams that form a roof's framework?

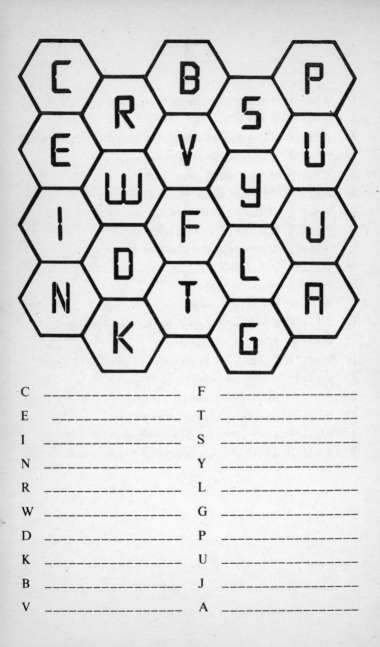

C _____   F _____

E _____   T _____
                       S _____
I _____   Y _____
N _____   L _____
R _____   G _____
W _____   P _____
D _____   U _____
K _____   J _____
B _____
V _____   A _____

C: What 'C' was prime minister from 1976 to 1979?

E: What 'E' is to try?

I: What 'I' is a volcanic island with ice-covered plateaux?

N: What 'N' means containing nitrogen?

R: What 'R' comes before hog, back and house?

W: What 'W' looked out on the Feast of Stephen?

D: What 'D' is the first portion of the small intestine?

K: What 'K' is a bird of prey and a toy that flies?

B: What 'B' is a red edible root used in salads?

V: What 'V' was American's deep space probe?

F: What 'F' means devil?

T: What 'T' is to shine with a flickering light?

S: What 'S' is a word that means the same as another?

Y: What 'Y' is the day just gone?

L: What 'L' means after proper time, recent and dead?

G: What 'G' is bizarre or absurdly distorted?

P: What 'P' is a sacred song or hymn?

U: What 'U' means hoofed?

J: What 'J' is a man's close-fitting jacket?

A: What 'A' was the son of Philip of Macedon?

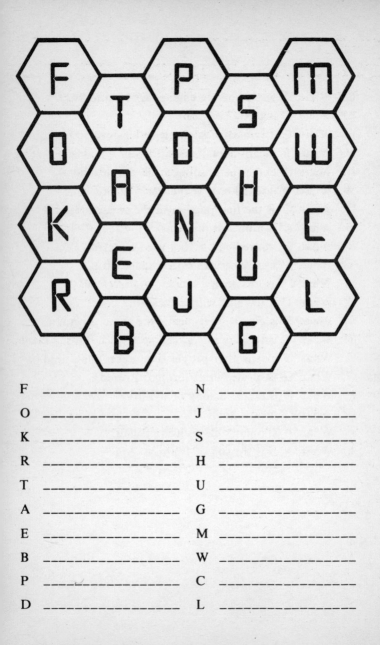

F _____ N _____

O _____ J _____

K _____ S _____

R _____ H _____

T _____ U _____

A _____ G _____

E _____ M _____

B _____ W _____

P _____ C _____

D _____ L _____

F: What 'F' comes before engine, lighter and bug?

O: What 'O' means stubborn?

K: What 'K' were German emperors?

R: What 'R' is primitive, violent, hearty – and offensive?

T: What 'T' is used as a solvent and paint thinner?

A: What 'A' is known as the 'Cotton State'?

E: What 'E' is the joint between fore and upper arm?

B: What 'B' is the 'Caped Crusader'?

P: What 'P' means fatherly?

D: What 'D' is a castle's subterranean cell?

N: What 'N' is neither masculine nor feminine?

J: What 'J' is the 'gentle' martial art?

S: What 'S' is a type of turnip?

H: What 'H' is an ungulate quadruped with flowing mane and tail?

U: What 'U' means worn by both sexes?

G: What 'G' is a cloth covering for legs below the knee?

M: What 'M' is the dawn?

W: What 'W' was fought on June 18, 1815?

C: What 'C' means cross-shaped?

L: What 'L' is a passionate expression of grief?

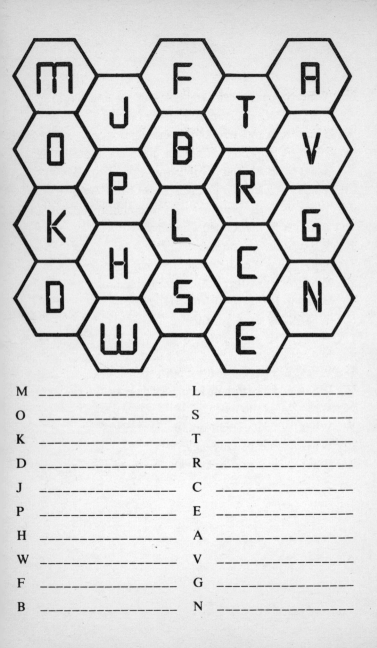

M _____

O _____

K _____

D _____

J _____

P _____

H _____

W _____

F _____

B _____

L _____

S _____

T _____

R _____

C _____

E _____

A _____

V _____

G _____

N _____

M: What 'M' is the study of fungi?

O: What 'O' comes before caste, back and doors?

K: What 'K' is an East African republic?

D: What 'D' is an edible kind of seaweed?

J: What 'J' is a wine bottle eight to twelve times normal size?

P: What 'P' literally means turn to stone?

H: What 'H' is exaggeration for the sake of emphasis?

W: What 'W' is a man who becomes a wolf?

F: What 'F' are the Polynesian islands of Tonga?

B: What 'B' is to strike repeatedly?

L: What 'L' is the form of public worship?

S: What 'S' is to wriggle or twist like a worm?

T: What 'T' is a hard metallic element with a very high melting point?

R: What 'R' is a straight slender stick?

C: What 'C' is to nestle together and hug?

E: What 'E' is to treat as equivalent?

A: What 'A' is the region covering southern Spain?

V: What 'V' was George III's grand-daughter?

G: What 'G' is a stringed instrument?

N: What 'N' means 'Great Land of the Rising Sun'?

C _____   B _____

I _____   Q _____

N _____   H _____

O _____   L _____

F _____   S _____

K _____   R _____

A _____   E _____

P _____   M _____

D _____   T _____

J _____   U _____

C: What 'C' is the currency of Brazil?

I: What 'I' is close and familiar?

N: What 'N' is a small sheltered place?

O: What 'O' are the innards of animals used as food?

F: What 'F' means containing iron?

K: What 'K' is an electric motor horn?

A: What 'A' is a market town in Hampshire?

P: What 'P' means treacherous?

D: What 'D' is the opposite of light?

J: What 'J' preceded rock 'n' roll?

B: What 'B' is to conduct oneself?

Q: What 'Q' is a misgiving or momentary queasiness?

H: What 'H' comes before sensitive, active and market?

L: What 'L' is fortune or chance?

S: What 'S' is to diverge abruptly from a regular line of motion?

R: What 'R' is a mouse-like rodent?

E: What 'E' is graceful, tasteful, refined?

M: What 'M' is half woman, half fish?

T: What 'T' is a treeless plain with permanently frozen subsoil?

U: What 'U' are the mammary glands of cattle?

G _____
Y _____
A _____
T _____
V _____
S _____
U _____
B _____
E _____
N _____

I _____
L _____
P _____
O _____
H _____
F _____
D _____
M _____
J _____
R _____

G: What 'G' is a disembodied spirit?

Y: What 'Y' is a toy you throw to come back?

A: What 'A' is a seafaring prince?

T: What 'T' means in accordance with fact?

V: What 'V' is Europe's longest river?

S: What 'S' is a formal meeting to decide ecclesiastical matters?

U: What 'U' means on?

B: What 'B' is a male who shares your parents?

E: What 'E' comes after rear, back and up?

N: What 'N' was Germany's National Socialist Party?

I: What 'I' is the anti-hero of Shakespeare's *Othello*?

L: What 'L' is idle?

P: What 'P' is to languish or waste away from grief?

O: What 'O' is a condensed form of oxygen with three atoms in each molecule?

H: What 'H' means towards this place?

F: What 'F' is someone or something deviating from the norm?

D: What 'D' is an Australian wild dog?

M: What 'M' is a disguise for the face?

J: What 'J' is another word for the god Jupiter?

R: What 'R' means boisterous?

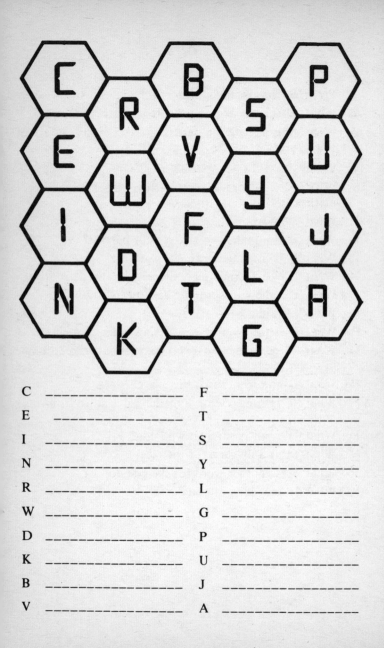

C _____   F _____

E _____   T _____

I _____   S _____

R _____   Y _____

W _____   L _____

D _____   G _____

K _____   P _____

B _____   U _____

V _____   J _____

                              A _____

C: What 'C' is a republic of north-central Africa?

E: What 'E' means and so on?

I: What 'I' is an irritating sensation in the upper surface of the skin?

N: What 'N' is a small measure of liquor?

R: What 'R' comes before snake, brain and trap?

W: What 'W' is a male witch or wizard?

D: What 'D' is a remarkably strong aluminium alloy?

K: What 'K' is an undergarment?

B: What 'B' means able to float or light-headed?

V: What 'V' is the decision of a jury?

F: What 'F' means stealthy or sneaky?

T: What 'T' is a cartoon cat?

S: What 'S' is sentence construction?

Y: What 'Y' is to deviate erratically from a course?

L: What 'L' is a large, edible, ten-legged marine crustacean?

G: What 'G' is the superlative of general?

P: What 'P' is inordinate self-esteem – and a group of lions?

U: What 'U' is the best of one's ability?

J: What 'J' is an ill-fated Shakespearean heroine?

A: What 'A' is a post-mortem?

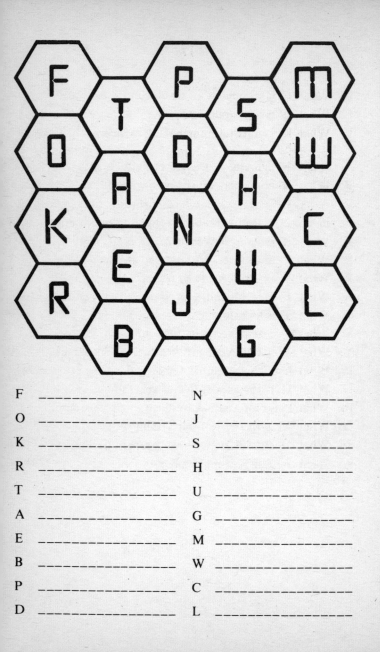

F _____   N _____

O _____   J _____

K _____   S _____

R _____   H _____

T _____   U _____

A _____   G _____

E _____   M _____

B _____   W _____

P _____   C _____

D _____   L _____

F: What 'F' is speedy?

O: What 'O' is egg-shaped or oval?

K: What 'K' is a furnace for baking or drying?

R: What 'R' is a Russian composer and pianist?

T: What 'T' comes before coat, table and stile?

A: What 'A' means at all times?

E: What 'E' is a Cumbrian river, a prime minister – and paradise?

B: What 'B' is slang for alcoholic drink?

P: What 'P' is a hymn of praise and thanksgiving?

D: What 'D' is also called the red-backed sandpiper?

N: What 'N' is the unoccupied area between opposing armies?

J: What 'J' is an African fetish?

S: What 'S' is a summary or brief outline?

H: What 'H' is a slight indication?

U: What 'U' is to make use of?

G: What 'G' is a leaf-bud?

M: What 'M' is long thick hair on the head?

W: What 'W' are German armed forces?

C: What 'C' is the feast of the Purification of the Virgin Mary?

L: What 'L' are the *sine qua non* in Blockbusters?

M _____   L _____

O _____   S _____

K _____   T _____

D _____   R _____

J _____   C _____

P _____   E _____

H _____   A _____

W _____   V _____

F _____   G _____

B _____   N _____

M: What 'M' means to increase in quantity, get up on – and display?

O: What 'O' was Hamlet's lady love?

K: What 'K' is the pool in some card games?

D: What 'D' is an academic dud?

J: What 'J' is a Boeing 747?

P: What 'P' comes before corn, eye and gun?

H: What 'H' is the hip or hind legs of a quadruped?

W: What 'W' is a furrow-like crease in the skin?

F: What 'F' is elaborate?

B: What 'B' is the federal capital of Switzerland?

L: What 'L' is the Light-Bringer or Morning Star?

S: What 'S' is water saturated with sugar?

T: What 'T' is inflicting pain as a means of persuasion?

R: What 'R' are wide, flat fishes with long spiky tails?

C: What 'C' is the apex or culmination?

E: What 'E' was the starship in *Star Trek*?

A: What 'A' means to relieve or mitigate?

V: What 'V' is the Greek goddess of love?

G: What 'G' is the constellation Castor and Pollux?

N: What 'N' is a tough and elastic synthetic fabric?

C _____   B _____

I _____   Q _____

N _____   H _____

O _____   L _____

F _____   S _____

K _____   R _____

A _____   E _____

P _____   M _____

D _____   T _____

J _____   U _____

C: What 'C' is a summons?

I: What 'I' is the opposite in order, direction or effect?

N: What 'N' comes before shell, hatch and house?

O: What 'O' is the beginning?

F: What 'F' is an enclosed apparatus in which heat is produced?

K: What 'K' is the hide of a young beast – and sleep?

A: What 'A' is to permit?

P: What 'P' is one who shows extreme propriety?

D: What 'D' is a beggar's wench or paramour?

J: What 'J' are blue denim trousers?

B: What 'B' is a friend?

Q: What 'Q' is a ring thrown to encircle a peg?

H: What 'H' was Nelson's first name?

L: What 'L' is an art museum in Paris?

S: What 'S' is the combination of separate elements into a whole?

R: What 'R' is an unsophisticated rural person?

E: What 'E' means roaming in quest of adventure?

M: What 'M' is a fish that climbs trees?

T: What 'T' is a political party whose name comes from the Irish for robber?

U: What 'U' is habitual?

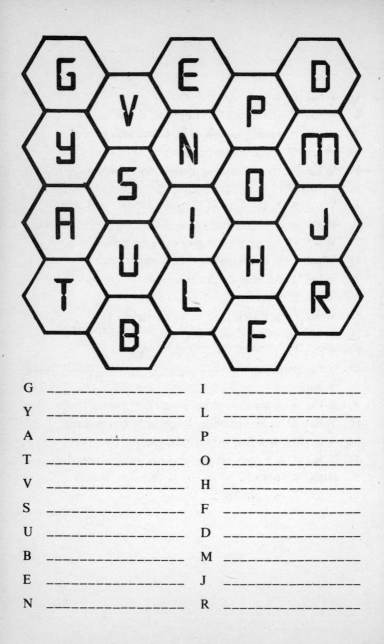

G _____

Y _____

A _____

T _____

V _____

S _____

U _____

B _____

E _____

N _____

I _____

L _____

P _____

O _____

H _____

F _____

D _____

M _____

J _____

R _____

G: What 'G' is a castrated horse?

Y: What 'Y' is a country bumpkin?

A: What 'A' called himself 'The Greatest'?

T: What 'T' comes before step, tone and way?

V: What 'V' means causing delight to the senses?

S: What 'S' is to cause to occur at the same time?

U: What 'U' is the womb?

B: What 'B' is a short fringe of hair – and a sudden loud noise?

E: What 'E' is the Highland Gaelic dialect?

N: What 'N' is to burrow into, or rub against, with your nose?

I: What 'I' is a bill?

L: What 'L' means attack verbally, beat or thrash?

P: What 'P' is swine-like or piggy?

O: What 'O' is the most abundant of all terrestrial elements?

H: What 'H' was a Roman satirist and poet?

F: What 'F' is useless or ineffectual?

D: What 'D' is an appointment, a time and a fruit?

M: What 'M' is a world-famous mouse?

J: What 'J' is a rock singer who gathers no moss?

R: What 'R' is to be boisterously jovial or frolic?

C _____   F _____

E _____   T _____

I _____   S _____

N _____   Y _____

R _____   L _____

W _____   G _____

D _____   P _____

K _____   U _____

B _____   J _____

V _____   A _____

C: What 'C' was US president from 1976 to 1981?

E: What 'E' is an old-fashioned word for marriage?

I: What 'I' is habitual or long-established?

N: What 'N' is a dolt or thick-head?

R: What 'R' comes before diamond, rider and house?

W: What 'W' is anger?

D: What 'D' is a brewer's cart without sides?

K: What 'K' is a twist in rope?

B: What 'B' is a large striped antelope – and a small tuned drum?

V: What 'V' is a symphonic English composer?

F: What 'F' is one of a ship's middle timbers?

T: What 'T' are used for mastication?

S: What 'S' is a spirit of the air – or slender girl?

Y: What 'Y' is to sing with frequent changes between normal voice and falsetto?

L: What 'L' is a German pistol?

G: What 'G' is to bend the knee in worship?

P: What 'P' means introduce, give – and offer for show?

U: What 'U' is a king who wrongfully assumes the throne?

J: What 'J' is a precious stone?

A: What 'A' was the Ugandan tyrant deposed in 1979?

F _____   N _____

O _____   J _____

K _____   S _____

R _____   H _____

T _____   U _____

A _____   G _____

E _____   M _____

B _____   W _____

P _____   C _____

D _____   L _____

F: What 'F' was dictator of Spain?

O: What 'O' is a fugitive from justice?

K: What 'K' is slang for exhausted?

R: What 'R' is an ornament of ribbons for horse's harness?

T: What 'T' means Hungarian gypsy?

A: What 'A' comes before fiend, bishop and enemy?

E: What 'E' comes after a gentleman's name?

B: What 'B' assassinated Julius Caesar?

P: What 'P' bleaches hair?

D: What 'D' is a sea-anchor?

N: What 'N' is a rough lump of precious metal?

J: What 'J' means to cast off unfeelingly?

S: What 'S' is a Jewish congregation?

H: What 'H' is a man's name that also means ravage?

U: What 'U' shows people to their seats?

G: What 'G' are the people next below the nobility in society?

M: What 'M' is a wooden hammer?

W: What 'W' is the official seat of the Lord Chancellor in the House of Lords?

C: What 'C' is coiled or twisted?

L: What 'L' is a wild cat with tufted ears?

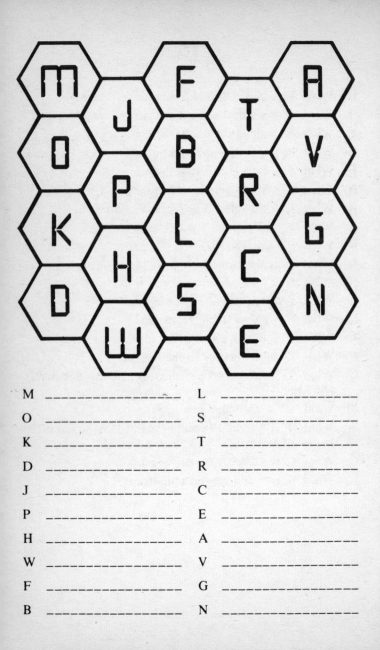

M _____ L _____
O _____ S _____
K _____ T _____
D _____ R _____
J _____ C _____
P _____ E _____
H _____ A _____
W _____ V _____
F _____ G _____
B _____ N _____

M: What 'M' was a top female pop singer of 1985?

O: What 'O' is a snow-leopard and a measure of weight?

K: What 'K' is an irresistible tendency to steal?

D: What 'D' is a Scandinavian kingdom?

J: What 'J' is to scoff?

P: What 'P' is a community's lowest class?

H: What 'H' comes before priest, rise and school?

W: What 'W' is a large red North American stag?

F: What 'F' wrote *The Day of The Jackal*?

B: What 'B' is meaningless chatter – and the murmur of water?

L: What 'L' is a soft fruit with a scaly covering?

S: What 'S' is to faint?

T: What 'T' are tartan trousers?

R: What 'R' is to undergo oxydisation?

C: What 'C' is an acrobat who twists him or herself into abnormal positions?

E: What 'E' is everlasting?

A: What 'A' is the shaft on which a wheel revolves?

V: What 'V' means capable of being wounded?

G: What 'G' is an Arabian spirit or goblin?

N: What 'N' is a writer's pen name?

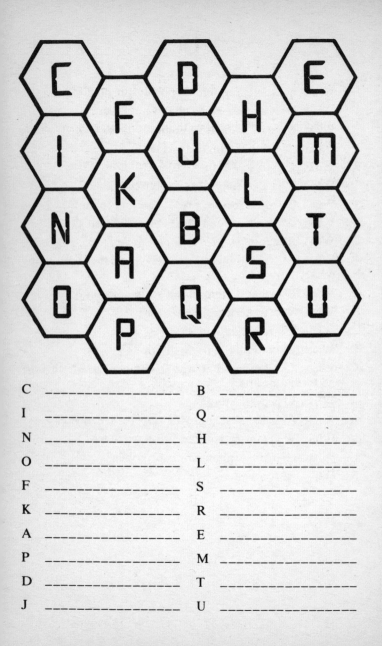

C _____   B _____

I _____   Q _____

N _____   H _____

O _____   L _____

F _____   S _____

K _____   R _____

A _____   E _____

P _____   M _____

D _____   T _____

J _____   U _____

C: What 'C' is a film using animated drawings?

I: What 'I' is to devise or originate?

N: What 'N' is a word used as the name of a person or thing?

O: What 'O' is Turkish?

F: What 'F' is fluff and down and slang for police?

K: What 'K' is a South African ravine or valley?

A: What 'A' is sky blue?

P: What 'P' comes before love, fat and dog?

D: What 'D' is a male duck?

J: What 'J' is the liquid part of vegetables or fruit?

B: What 'B' is sick or nauseous?

Q: What 'Q' means completely – or only moderately?

H: What 'H' is an air-cushion vehicle?

L: What 'L' is an illegal execution by a mob?

S: What 'S' is to barter one thing for another?

R: What 'R' is the sound of dry leaves in motion?

E: What 'E' is an administrator in the Common Market?

M: What 'M' is a world featherweight boxing champion?

T: What 'T' is an oppressive or cruel ruler?

U: What 'U' means like a bear?

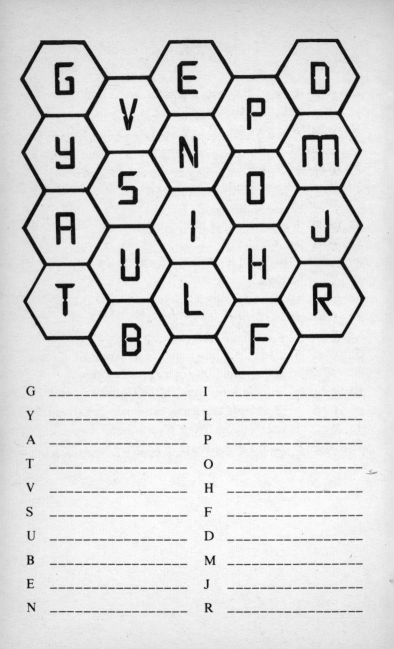

G _____   I _____

Y _____   L _____

A _____   P _____

T _____   O _____

V _____   H _____

S _____   F _____

U _____   D _____

B _____   M _____

E _____   J _____

N _____   R _____

18

G: What 'G' is a kind of civet cat?

Y: What 'Y' is to bark shrilly or fussily?

A: What 'A' is a pointed tool for making small holes?

T: What 'T' is the exact counterpart of a person or thing?

V: What 'V' was an 18th century Italian composer?

S: What 'S' is a Eurasian maple tree?

U: What 'U' means of a town or city?

B: What 'B' is coarse canvas?

E: What 'E' comes before mural, ordinary and terrestrial?

N: What 'N' is common sense?

I: What 'I' is drunkenness?

L: What 'L' is the pale fluid resembling blood plasma?

P: What 'P' was the king of rock 'n' roll?

O: What 'O' is to refuse to have social contact with?

H: What 'H' is a vacuum cleaner?

F: What 'F is an Andalusian gypsy dance?

D: What 'D' is an idler – or male honey bee?

M: What 'M' is President of France?

J: What 'J' is to protrude?

R: What 'R' is a girl's name meaning pity or compassion?

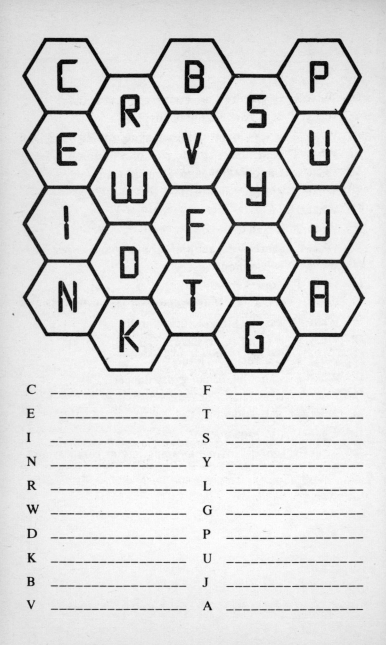

C _____
E _____
I _____
N _____
R _____
W _____
D _____
K _____
B _____
V _____

F _____
T _____
S _____
Y _____
L _____
G _____
P _____
U _____
J _____
A _____

C: What 'C' is to make something sore by rubbing?

E: What 'E' is mercy killing?

I: What 'I' is a long peninsular extending into the Mediterranean?

N: What 'N' is a local anaesthetic?

R: What 'R' is a bit of bread taken from a loaf and rebaked?

W: What 'W' provides the means of flight?

D: What 'D' is an aborigine of Borneo?

K: What 'K' is smoked herring?

B: What 'B' is slang for your head?

V: What 'V' means fox-like?

F: What 'F' is a scarlet-feathered bird with long legs and neck?

T: What 'T' is an oriental head-dress?

S: What 'S' comes before dance, fish and stick?

Y: What 'Y' is an inhabitant of New England?

L: What 'L' is luxuriant, sumptuous – and a drunk?

G: What 'G' is headquarters of the WHO and the Red Cross?

P: What 'P' means fussy and fastidious?

U: What 'U' is a tumult or violent disturbance?

J: What 'J' means barely – and fair?

A: What 'A' is uncle-like?

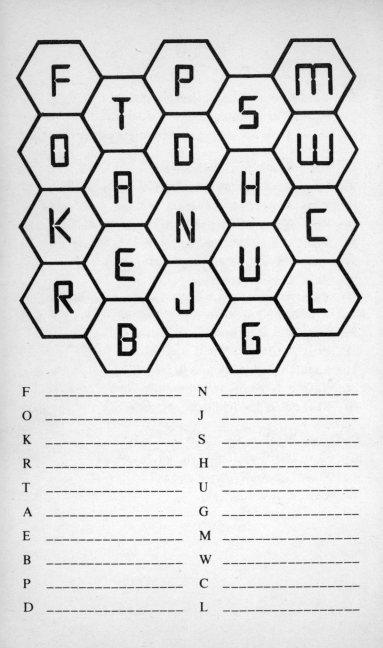

F	_____	N	_____
O	_____	J	_____
K	_____	S	_____
R	_____	H	_____
T	_____	U	_____
A	_____	G	_____
E	_____	M	_____
B	_____	W	_____
P	_____	C	_____
D	_____	L	_____

F: What 'F' is lacking resilience and flaccid?

O: What 'O' is an expression of sudden pain?

K: What 'K' are short baggy trousers gathered in at the knee?

R: What 'R' is a wiley subterfuge?

T: What 'T' are minute tongs for picking up small objects?

A: What 'A' means pertaining to birds?

E: What 'E' is pleasing to the ear?

B: What 'B' is the chemistry concerned with organisms?

P: What 'P' is an oriental sacred building?

D: What 'D' is indigestion?

N: What 'N' comes before reel, stand and agent?

J: What 'J' are a body of persons sworn to render a verdict?

S: What 'S' is someone who studies especially hard?

H: What 'H' is very large?

U: What 'U' is to cover furniture with fabric?

G: What 'G' is a West African republic?

M: What 'M' was a Philippino dictator?

W: What 'W' do you tell a horse?

C: What 'C' is part of a song recurring at intervals?

L: What 'L' is to lie hidden with evil intent?

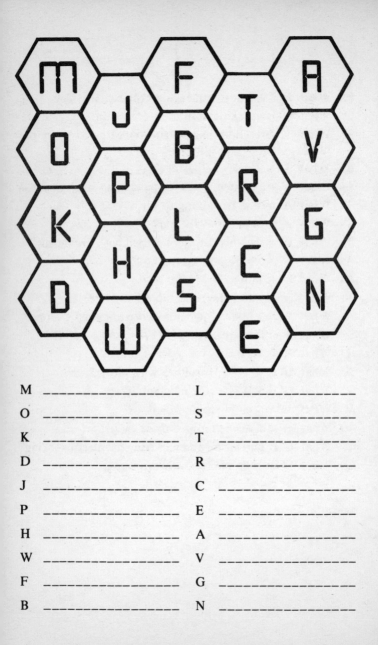

M _____
O _____
K _____
D _____
J _____
P _____
H _____
W _____
F _____
B _____

L _____
S _____
T _____
R _____
C _____
E _____
A _____
V _____
G _____
N _____

M: What 'M' is the officer ranked just below lieutenant-colonel?

O: What 'O' means professed or declared?

K: What 'K' is a small hill or mound?

D: What 'D' was the heroine of Shakespeare's *Othello*?

J: What 'J' is a flexion and sudden muscular extension of legs?

P: What 'P' means tediously wordy?

H: What 'H' is a snooker player nicknamed 'Hurricane'?

W: What 'W' was an 19th century political party?

F: What 'F' sold his soul to the devil?

B: What 'B' means pastoral?

L: What 'L' is a cross between a collie and a greyhound?

S: What 'S' comes before board, blade and back?

T: What 'T' is an ice-cream of mixed fruits?

R: What 'R' is the smallest animal of a litter?

C: What 'C' is the Messiah?

E: What 'E' is high praise?

A: What 'A' is a pear-shaped tropical fruit?

V: What 'V' is the Roman god of fire and metal-working?

G: What 'G' is both relevant and appropriate?

N: What 'N' is the cathedral of Paris?

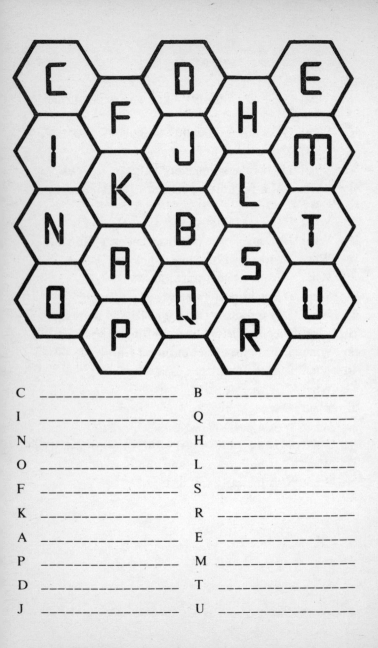

C _____   B _____

I _____   Q _____

N _____   H _____

O _____   L _____

F _____   S _____

K _____   R _____

A _____   E _____

P _____   M _____

D _____   T _____

J _____   U _____

C: What 'C' is the short sharp note of a small bird?

I: What 'I' is to make better?

N: What 'N' is the kingdom on the southern slopes of the Himalayas?

O: What 'O' is a large, fish-eating hawk?

F: What 'F' is a lively Spanish dance?

K: What 'K' comes after slip, granny and reef?

A: What 'A' means askew or twisted?

P: What 'P' is to go the rounds of a garrison?

D: What 'D' is a cartoon duck?

J: What 'J' is a political council or committee?

B: What 'B' is mild, gracious and not malignant?

Q: What 'Q' is pleasingly old-fashioned?

H: What 'H' comes before brained, lip and bell?

L: What 'L' is a rheumatic affliction of the lower back?

S: What 'S' is to attempt to hit – or to steal?

R: What 'R' is the currency of India?

E: What 'E' is to cry out?

M: What 'M' is an obsolete infantryman's gun?

T: What 'T' is a large American fowl related to the pheasant?

U: What 'U' is a soothing or healing salve?

G _____ I _____

Y _____ L _____

A _____ P _____

T _____ O _____

V _____ H _____

S _____ F _____

U _____ D _____

B _____ M _____

E _____ J _____

N _____ R _____

G: What 'G' was the tenth member of the EEC?

Y: What 'Y' is an edible tuber of a tropical climbing plant?

A: What 'A' means unwilling or antipathetic?

T: What 'T' is a gas or water driven rotary engine?

V: What 'V' is a solemn promise?

S: What 'S' is the mutually beneficial association of dissimilar life forms?

U: What 'U' means to howl or hoot?

B: What 'B' is a fundamental?

E: What 'E' is a small supernatural creature?

N: What 'N' comes before drip, stick, existent and fiction?

I: What 'I' is the republic created in 1945?

L: What 'L' is an ear, a sail – and a large marine worm?

P: What 'P' is one who is zealous on behalf of his country?

O: What 'O' comes before draft, land and seas?

H: What 'H' was an indecisive Danish prince?

F: What 'F' is that which is going to happen?

D: What 'D' is a down-filled quilt?

M: What 'M' is a Greek dish of minced meat and aubergine?

J: What 'J' is an account of day-to-day events?

R: What 'R' is Europe's largest seaport?

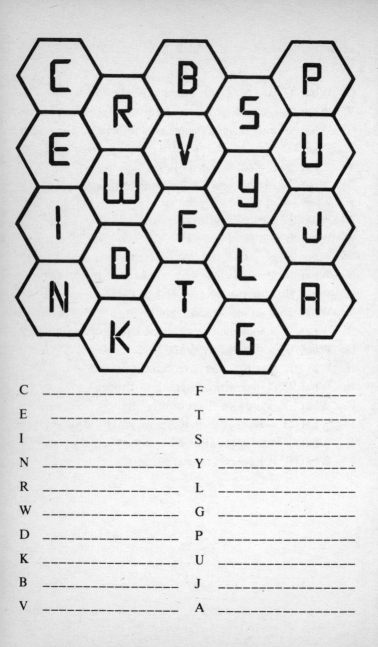

C _____ F _____

E _____ T _____

I _____ S _____

N _____ Y _____

R _____ L _____

W _____ G _____

D _____ P _____

K _____ U _____

B _____ J _____

V _____ A _____

C: What 'C' is a long green vegetable eaten in salads?

E: What 'E' was heaven in Greek mythology?

I: What 'I' is to stamp, influence deeply – and force into service?

N: What 'N' means addictive drug?

R: What 'R' lies between Bulgaria and the USSR?

W: What 'W' stays liquid when the rest of the milk curdles?

D: What 'D' created Mickey Mouse?

K: What 'K' is the currency of Sweden and a margarine?

B: What 'B' is a serious disease of cattle and human beings?

V: What 'V' is a mass of whirling fluid?

F: What 'F' is a spiny, yellow-flowered evergreen shrub?

T: What 'T' is a large spider?

S: What 'S' is a cavalry sword with a curved blade?

Y: What 'Y' was an Irish poet?

L: What 'L' comes before land, down and brow?

G: What 'G' is a disease-causing micro-organism?

P: What 'P' is the gloss produced by age on woodwork?

U: What 'U' assumes liability for an insurance policy?

J: What 'J' is a Chinese idol?

A: What 'A' is a luminous atmospheric phenomenon?

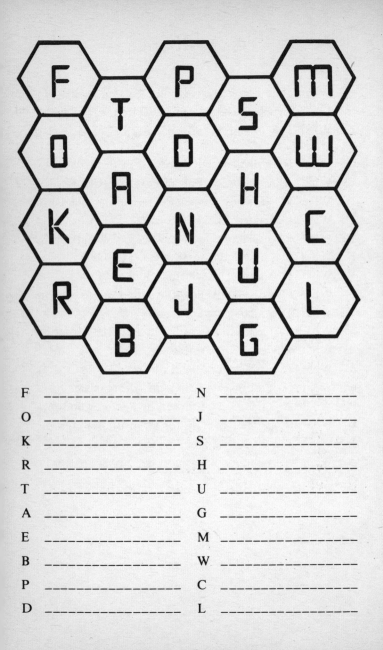

F   _____

O   _____

K   _____

R   _____

T   _____

A   _____

E   _____

B   _____

P   _____

D   _____

N   _____

J   _____

S   _____

H   _____

U   _____

G   _____

M   _____

W   _____

C   _____

L   _____

F: What 'F' is one-eighth of a mile?

O: What 'O' is treatment of illness by manipulation of bones?

K: What 'K' is a small knob?

R: What 'R' is one of the two chief forms of football?

T: What 'T' is a plant of the ginger family used in curry powder?

A: What 'A' is an instrument for cleaning ears?

E: What 'E' means come from or emerge?

B: What 'B' are gas bubbles in a scuba diver's body?

P: What 'P' is a communal dialect?

D: What 'D' is long-lasting?

N: What 'N' is a strip of dough – and a simpleton?

J: What 'J' is someone who brings bad luck?

S: What 'S' is England's greatest dramatist?

H: What 'H' is an involuntary spasm of respiratory organs?

U: What 'U' personifies the United States?

G: What 'G' comes before ale, bread and nut?

M: What 'M' means short-sighted?

W: What 'W' is a famous architect, a small bird – and a member of the navy?

C: What 'C' is apple brandy?

L: What 'L' is money – especially when filthy?

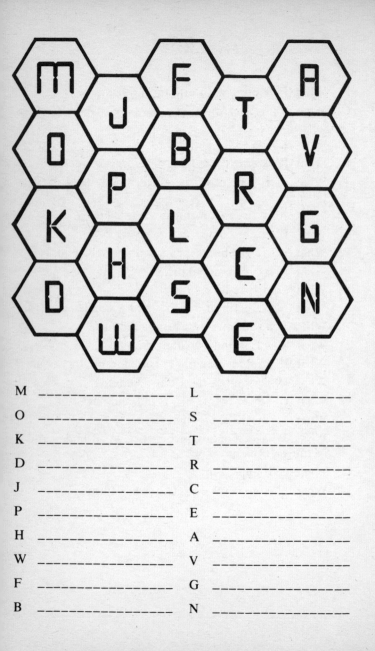

M _ _ _ _ _ _ _ _ _ _ _ _ _ _ _ _ 	L _ _ _ _ _ _ _ _ _ _ _ _ _ _ _

O _ _ _ _ _ _ _ _ _ _ _ _ _ _ _ _ 	S _ _ _ _ _ _ _ _ _ _ _ _ _ _ _

K _ _ _ _ _ _ _ _ _ _ _ _ _ _ _ _ 	T _ _ _ _ _ _ _ _ _ _ _ _ _ _ _

D _ _ _ _ _ _ _ _ _ _ _ _ _ _ _ _ 	R _ _ _ _ _ _ _ _ _ _ _ _ _ _ _

J _ _ _ _ _ _ _ _ _ _ _ _ _ _ _ _ 	C _ _ _ _ _ _ _ _ _ _ _ _ _ _ _

P _ _ _ _ _ _ _ _ _ _ _ _ _ _ _ _ 	E _ _ _ _ _ _ _ _ _ _ _ _ _ _ _

H _ _ _ _ _ _ _ _ _ _ _ _ _ _ _ _ 	A _ _ _ _ _ _ _ _ _ _ _ _ _ _ _

W _ _ _ _ _ _ _ _ _ _ _ _ _ _ _ _ 	V _ _ _ _ _ _ _ _ _ _ _ _ _ _ _

F _ _ _ _ _ _ _ _ _ _ _ _ _ _ _ _ 	G _ _ _ _ _ _ _ _ _ _ _ _ _ _ _

B _ _ _ _ _ _ _ _ _ _ _ _ _ _ _ _ 	N _ _ _ _ _ _ _ _ _ _ _ _ _ _ _

M: What 'M' is a black bird that can learn to talk?

O: What 'O' is an award for cinematic achievement?

K: What 'K' is the world's largest bear?

D: What 'D' is a waterless, treeless region?

J: What 'J' is psychologically immature?

P: What 'P' is the bow of a ship?

H: What 'H' is an aircraft that derives lift from rotors?

W: What 'W' is a spiral-shelled marine mollusc?

F: What 'F' is an old sweetheart?

B: What 'B' is a lord of the realm?

L: What 'L' means to moo like a cow?

S: What 'S' is mixed raw vegetables?

T: What 'T' is an abnormal growth or swelling?

R: What 'R' is waste fragments of brick or stone?

C: What 'C' equals Celsius?

E: What 'E' was Napoleon's first island of exile?

A: What 'A' comes before graph, mobile and biography?

V: What 'V' is a colourless spirit distilled from rye?

G: What 'G' is a small prickly fruit used for pickling?

N: What 'N' is something not easily classified?

C _____   B _____

I _____   Q _____

N _____   H _____

O _____   L _____

F _____   S _____

K _____   R _____

A _____   E _____

P _____   M _____

D _____   T _____

J _____   U _____

27

C: What 'C' is the world's premier dog show?

I: What 'I' are goods introduced from a foreign country?

N: What 'N' is someone in their nineties?

O: What 'O' is a straight-horned African antelope?

F: What 'F' is to roll up a sail?

K: What 'K' is a native of Kurdistan?

A: What 'A' is an emanation or atmosphere?

P: What 'P' is sharp-pointed, piquant or caustic?

D: What 'D' is a machine that converts mechanical into electrical energy?

J: What 'J' is a fibre used for sacking – and a Germanic invader of England?

B: What 'B' is an inflatable rubber bag?

Q: What 'Q' is bizarre, unwell – and homosexual?

H: What 'H' is a trusted follower?

L: What 'L' is the milky fluid rubber comes from?

S: What 'S' is a Japanese drink made from fermented rice?

R: What 'R' is an animal that chews the cud?

E: What 'E' is a vast Florida marsh?

M: What 'M' comes before pie, lark and guard?

T: What 'T' is teaching?

U: What 'U' was a World War II submarine?

G _____
Y _____
A _____
T _____
V _____
S _____
U _____
B _____
E _____
N _____

I _____
L _____
P _____
O _____
H _____
F _____
D _____
M _____
J _____
R _____

28

G: What 'G' is a kind of butter made in India?

Y: What 'Y' is a divided republic on the Arabian peninsula?

A: What 'A' means alternatively attracted and repelled?

T: What 'T' is a plant with bright-coloured, bell-shaped flowers?

V: What 'V' is empty, vacant – and invalid?

S: What 'S' is a highly seasoned sausage?

U: What 'U' is a radio frequency?

B: What 'B' is a flat, blood-sucking insect infesting beds?

E: What 'E' comes after Lent?

N: What 'N' means a person of no importance?

I: What 'I' is the force with which a body moves?

L: What 'L' is a kind of pasta dish?

P: What 'P' is a short-legged, flat-faced dog with silky hair?

O: What 'O' is a child whose parents are dead?

H: What 'H' is an intuitive feeling?

F: What 'F' means of public revenue?

D: What 'D' is a projecting window in a sloping roof?

M: What 'M' is dumb?

J: What 'J' is a locomotive crane, a billiards stroke, and a wren?

R: What 'R' is a highly polluted German river?

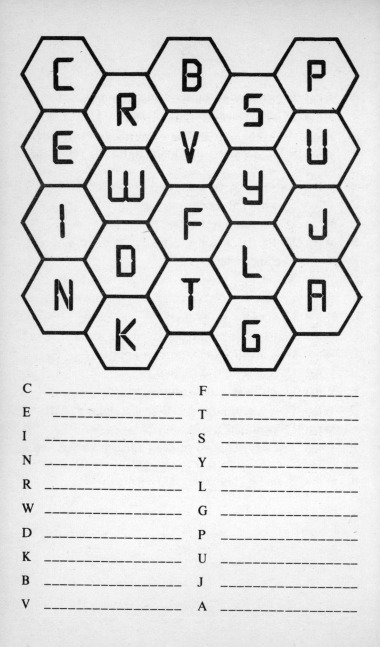

C _____ F _____
E _____ T _____
I _____ S _____
N _____ Y _____
R _____ L _____
W _____ G _____
D _____ P _____
K _____ U _____
B _____ J _____
V _____ A _____

29

C: What 'C' comes before paper, steel and copy?

E: What 'E' means exhausted and feeble?

I: What 'I' is something surgically inserted in living tissue?

N: What 'N' means existing in name only?

R: What 'R' is a rare precious stone?

W: What 'W' is a loading platform for ships?

D: What 'D' means to do with the back?

K: What 'K' is glory or renown?

B: What 'B' is a barefoot, world record runner?

V: What 'V' means giving birth to live young?

F: What 'F' is polecat hair?

T: What 'T' is a vigorous pull and a tow boat?

S: What 'S' is to sweat, or be faint, from heat?

Y: What 'Y' is a European socialist republic?

L: What 'L' is the primary form of animals that undergo metamorphosis?

G: What 'G' is someone of extraordinary size?

P: What 'P' means headlong or recklessly?

U: What 'U' are foods which Jews do not eat?

J: What 'J' is the awarding of what is due?

A: What 'A' means original or genuine?

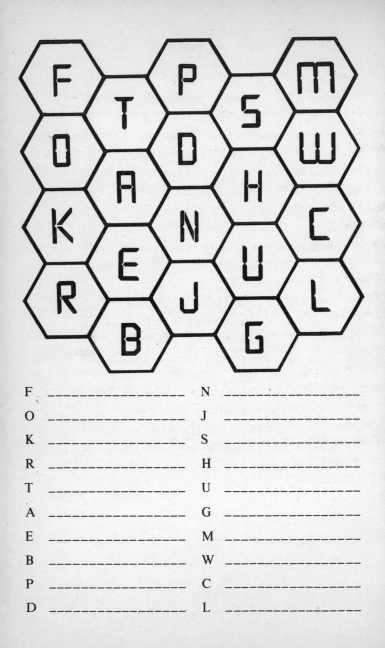

F _____   N _____

O _____   J _____

K _____   S _____

R _____   H _____

T _____   U _____

A _____   G _____

E _____   M _____

B _____   W _____

P _____   C _____

D _____   L _____

30

F: What 'F' comes before pond, tail and hook?

O: What 'O' is to swing back and forth like a pendulum?

K: What 'K' is Russian rye-beer?

R: What 'R' is a girl's name and fragrant herb?

T: What 'T' is a three-legged stool or stand?

A: What 'A' is absolute government?

E: What 'E' is an outgoing person?

B: What 'B' is a creeping plant, a musical instrument – and a glass bead?

P: What 'P' means transparent or clear?

D: What 'D' is an aimless scrawl?

N: What 'N' was a 16th century French prophet?

J: What 'J' is to place side by side?

S: What 'S' is a Hindu religious teacher?

H: What 'H' is a knapsack?

U: What 'U' is fever which goes up and down?

G: What 'G' is meaningless sounds?

M: What 'M' is a marine bivalve mollusc?

W: What 'W' comes before force, top and shop?

C: What 'C' is a Chinese dish of noodles and shredded meat?

L: What 'L' is a poetic word for forlorn?

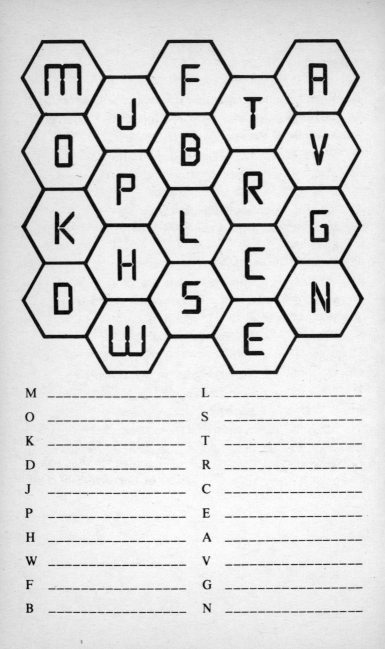

M _____

O _____

K _____

D _____

J _____

P _____

H _____

W _____

F _____

B _____

L _____

S _____

T _____

R _____

C _____

E _____

A _____

V _____

G _____

N _____

31

M: What 'M' is the compulsory roadworthiness test for cars?

O: What 'O' comes before season, verdict and university?

K: What 'K' is a kind of cole or cabbage?

D: What 'D' is a bullet that expands on impact?

J: What 'J' are the mountains between France and Switzerland?

P: What 'P' is an edible seed – and rhythmic throbbing?

H: What 'H' was the last divine Japanese emperor?

W: What 'W' is a wild herb growing where it is not wanted?

F: What 'F' means bounded and limited?

B: What 'B' are almost one quarter of all mammals?

L: What 'L' is a medicinal or cosmetic liquid for external use?

S: What 'S' is booty carried off by burglars?

T: What 'T' is a triangular framework of beams and a belt worn for a hernia?

R: What 'R' is the family of a king?

C: What 'C' is a supersonic airliner?

E: What 'E' means luxuriantly prolific?

A: What 'A' is to foretell the future from omens?

V: What 'V' provided the historical model for Dracula?

G: What 'G' is plain weave cotton or linen cloth of dyed yarn?

N: What 'N' is a halo?

C _____

I _____

N _____

O _____

F _____

K _____

A _____

P _____

D _____

J _____

B _____

Q _____

H _____

L _____

S _____

R _____

E _____

M _____

T _____

U _____

32

C: What 'C' is a tallow or wax cylinder that gives light?

I: What 'I' means with your identity concealed?

N: What 'N' comes before stick, starter and stop?

O: What 'O' was a stableman at an inn?

F: What 'F' is an open fruit tart?

K: What 'K' is a Chinese gesture of absolute submission?

A: What 'A' is to worship?

P: What 'P' is fabric placed to conceal curtain fixtures?

D: What 'D' is a shapeless lump of food?

J: What 'J' is the berry used in making gin?

B: What 'B' is muscular strength?

Q: What 'Q' is a proportional part or share?

H: What 'H' is capital of Finland?

L: What 'L' is a gramophone record played at 33⅓ rpm?

S: What 'S' means irritable, sullen and churlish?

R: What 'R' is a mountain oak?

E: What 'E' is a small hole in cloth or a loophole?

M: What 'M' is a slimy exudation?

T: What 'T' is a short club or cudgel?

U: What 'U' comes before Kingdom and States?

G _____
Y _____
A _____
T _____
V _____
S _____
U _____
B _____
E _____
N _____

I _____
L _____
P _____
O _____
H _____
F _____
D _____
M _____
J _____
R _____

33

G: What 'G' are rubber overshoes?

Y: What 'Y' is a Canadian and Alaskan river?

A: What 'A' is a lawyer or advocate?

T: What 'T' is slang for extreme left-winger and diarrhoea?

V: What 'V' is sulphuric acid or any of its salts?

S: What 'S' comes before scribe, marine and stance?

U: What 'U' is a 13 km Cumbrian lake?

B: What 'B' is a dark or suntanned complexion?

E: What 'E' is a young hawk taken from the nest for training?

N: What 'N' is a quid?

I: What 'I' is deceptive or unreal?

L: What 'L' is a small bright parrot?

P: What 'P' are fireworks?

O: What 'O' is the path described by one body revolving around another?

H: What 'H' is a French bean?

F: What 'F' is a game where players hit the ball with their hands?

D: What 'D' is to confer a knighthood?

M: What 'M' is the fur of the muskrat?

J: What 'J' is a coin-operated music player?

R: What 'R' is Russia's monetary unit?

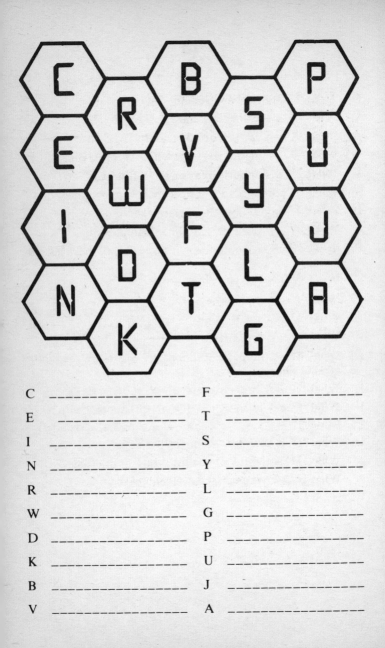

C _____

E _____

I _____

N _____

R _____

W _____

D _____

K _____

B _____

V _____

F _____

T _____

S _____

Y _____

L _____

G _____

P _____

U _____

J _____

A _____

34

C: What 'C' was a stuttering Roman emperor?

E: What 'E' means to ooze out or give off?

I: What 'I' is to dip in liquid?

N: What 'N' means execution by drowning?

R: What 'R' is a masseur, two games and an eraser?

W: What 'W' is an English cheese?

D: What 'D' is someone habitually drunk?

K: What 'K' is a fortified tower?

B: What 'B' is tinned beef, a hockey play – and a petty tyrant?

V: What 'V' means to convert into glass?

F: What 'F' destroys fungus?

T: What 'T' is a pig's foot?

S: What 'S' is a party to a lawsuit, or petitioner?

Y: What 'Y' is a light vessel used for pleasure trips and racing?

L: What 'L' comes after make, play for and fall in?

G: What 'G' is a structure criminals are hanged on?

P: What 'P' is glass that is heat and chemical resistant?

U: What 'U' is a centre for higher learning?

J: What 'J' is a desert of sweetened curds and whey?

A: What 'A' is a protection or shield?

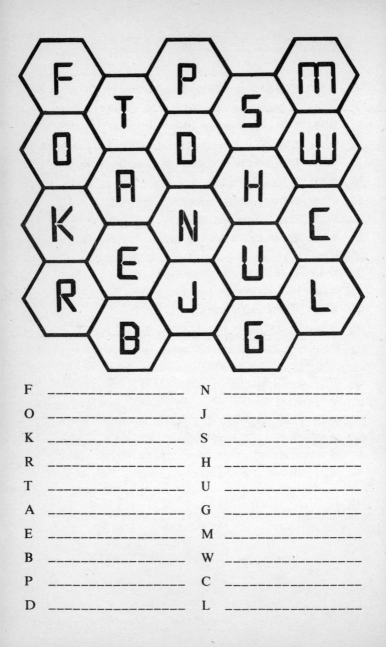

F _____ N _____

O _____ J _____

K _____ S _____

R _____ H _____

T _____ U _____

A _____ G _____

E _____ M _____

B _____ W _____

P _____ C _____

D _____ L _____

35

F: What 'F' is a stock of something ready to be drawn on?

O: What 'O' is a receptacle for bones, or charnel house?

K: What 'K' is a martial art like Kung Fu?

R: What 'R' is an American word for recruit or beginner?

T: What 'T' is a rich chocolate – and wrinkled fungus?

A: What 'A' is the first day of Lent?

E: What 'E' is the space over which a thing extends?

B: What 'B' is toilet-paper?

P: What 'P' is a gentle golf stroke?

D: What 'D' comes before fight, cart and tired?

N: What 'N' is harmful or unwholesome?

J: What 'J' is the slack flesh of the lower jaw?

S: What 'S' is a moslem sovereign?

H: What 'H' is rear – and a deer?

U: What 'U' has 157 member states?

G: What 'G' is a chess opening or stratagem?

M: What 'M' imparts motion?

W: What 'W' is a small red-brown carnivore like a stoat?

C: What 'C' is prevailing weather?

L: What 'L' are underpants extending to the ankles?

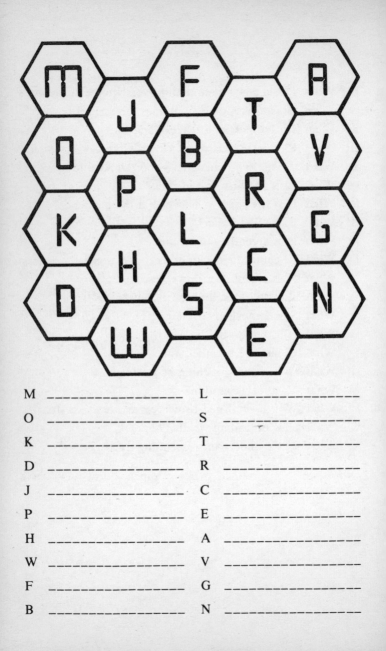

M _____   L _____

O _____   S _____

K _____   T _____

D _____   R _____

J _____   C _____

P _____   E _____

H _____   A _____

W _____   V _____

F _____   G _____

B _____   N _____

36

M: What 'M' is new wine, mould and a frenzied elephant's state?

O: What 'O' is lots and lots and lots?

K: What 'K' is one-hundredth of a rouble?

D: What 'D' is the enclosure in court for prisoners?

J: What 'J' is a very short time?

P: What 'P' is a heap of combustible material?

H: What 'H' comes before bitten, core and board?

W: What 'W' is to form fabric from thread?

F: What 'F' is a stuffy atmosphere?

B: What 'B' is unexpected prosperity – and an old TV series?

L: What 'L' comes before Mayor, Lieutenant and ship?

S: What 'S' is hard fat around the kidneys in beef or mutton?

T: What 'T' is a bed that slides beneath a higher bed?

R: What 'R' is a colony of penguins or seals?

C: What 'C' failed to turn back the tide?

E: What 'E' is a species that has died out?

A: What 'A' is a wind-activated harp?

V: What 'V' is built on islets and gradually sinking?

G: What 'G' kills germs?

N: What 'N' is a small drink, a pinch – and slang for a Japanese person?

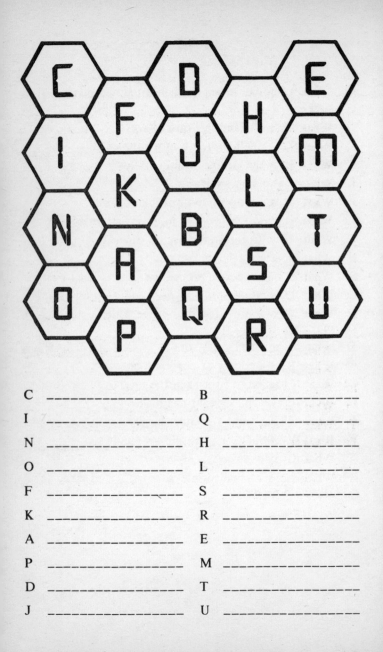

C _____ B _____

I _____ Q _____

N _____ H _____

O _____ L _____

F _____ S _____

K _____ R _____

A _____ E _____

P _____ M _____

D _____ T _____

J _____ U _____

37

C: What 'C' comes before feed, hearted and pox?

I: What 'I' is without delay?

N: What 'N' was a 19th century German philosopher?

O: What 'O' is an enclosure with fruit trees?

F: What 'F' is something cobbled together – and a sweet?

K: What 'K' is an Eskimo canoe?

A: What 'A' is the first sign of the Zodiac?

P: What 'P' comes before button, chair and bike?

D: What 'D' is an equatorial region of calms?

J: What 'J' is danger?

B: What 'B' was a Liverpool band?

Q: What 'Q' is five children born at one birth?

H: What 'H' is a boat that lifts out of the water at speed?

L: What 'L' means talkative?

S: What 'S' was a woman who agitated for the right to vote?

R: What 'R' is a gypsy?

E: What 'E' means to go off with a loud noise?

M: What 'M' is to eat with considerable jaw action?

T: What 'T' was a Russian revolutionary under Lenin?

U: What 'U' flows past Newport to the Bristol Channel?

G _____	I _____
Y _____	L _____
A _____	P _____
T _____	O _____
V _____	H _____
S _____	F _____
U _____	D _____
B _____	M _____
E _____	J _____
N _____	R _____

38

G: What 'G' is necrosis with decomposition of part of the body?

Y: What 'Y' is a lemon-coloured bird of the bunting family?

A: What 'A' is a poetic word for rustic paradise?

T: What 'T' is victorious?

V: What 'V' is a calling to a career or occupation?

S: What 'S' comes before tax, sonic and structure?

U: What 'U' is the racecourse between Derby and Stoke-on-Trent?

B: What 'B' is a TV quiz?

E: What 'E' is someone with special skill or knowledge?

N: What 'N' is a silvery element – and a US coin?

I: What 'I' means drink in?

L: What 'L' is to run with long, bounding strides?

P: What 'P' is a prize of money – and a small bag?

O: What 'O' is a very heavy metal of the platinum group?

H: What 'H' is a group of females associated with one male?

F: What 'F' is a hidden defect – and a squall of wind?

D: What 'D' was a Victorian Prime Minister?

M: What 'M' is a contractile fibrous band that produces movement?

J: What 'J' is a small Spanish horse?

R: What 'R' is a device producing a fulcrum for an oar?

C _____
E _____
I _____
N _____
R _____
W _____
D _____
K _____
B _____
V _____

F _____
T _____
S _____
Y _____
L _____
G _____
P _____
U _____
J _____
A _____

39

C: What 'C' was an Italian navigator?

E: What 'E' is a car's expulsion of the biproducts of combustion?

I: What 'I' comes before planting, view and pose?

N: What 'N' is a shallow recess in a wall?

R: What 'R' is a French ewe's milk cheese?

W: What 'W' means to make, or become, crooked?

D: What 'D' is a conduit or tube for conveying liquid?

K: What 'K' is a Jewish mourner's prayer?

B: What 'B' is a receptacle and an evergreen shrub?

V: What 'V' is a season's produce of grapes?

F: What 'F' comes before bag, bite and pit?

T: What 'T' is a flat-bladed tool for spreading mortar?

S: What 'S' is undressed kid?

Y: What 'Y' is the Belgian site of World War I battles?

L: What 'L' is lower on one side than the other?

G: What 'G' is a long-armed ape?

P: What 'P' is a contrivance designed to test your ingenuity?

U: What 'U' is the most northerly Shetland Island?

J: What 'J' is a kind of Welsh Methodist – and a loose garment?

A: What 'A' is Sagittarius?

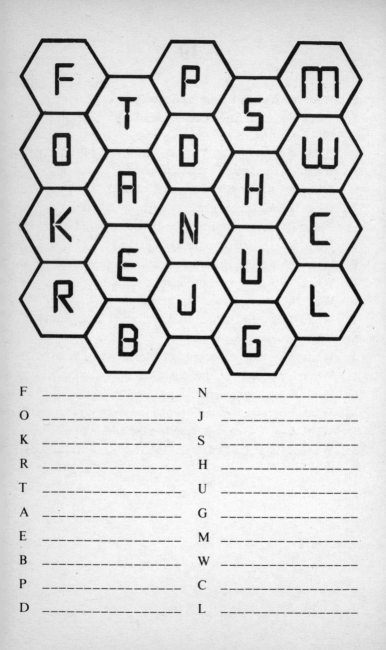

F _____   N _____

O _____   J _____

K _____   S _____

R _____   H _____

T _____   U _____

A _____   G _____

E _____   M _____

B _____   W _____

P _____   C _____

D _____   L _____

40

F: What 'F' is a drab, old-fashioned woman?

O: What 'O' is a bushy, mint-related herb?

K: What 'K' is the largest known bat?

R: What 'R' comes before empire, numeral and Catholic?

T: What 'T' is the edible stomach tissue of cows?

A: What 'A' is a bower or shady retreat?

E: What 'E' is the day before – and first woman?

B: What 'B' comes before bean, knife and fingers?

P: What 'P' is a long strip of cloth worn around lower legs?

D: What 'D' was Mussolini known as?

N: What 'N' comes before World, born, Year and moon?

J: What 'J' is to cross the street regardless of traffic?

S: What 'S' is the sugar occurring in most plants?

H: What 'H' is Egyptian privet used on hair?

U: What 'U' is the financial centre of the Netherlands?

G: What 'G' means to open wide – or stare curiously?

M: What 'M' is a source of artistic inspiration?

W: What 'W' is very small?

C: What 'C' is a Christmas song?

L: What 'L' is a dried seed pod used as a rough sponge?

M _____	L _____
O _____	S _____
K _____	T _____
D _____	R _____
J _____	C _____
P _____	E _____
H _____	A _____
W _____	V _____
F _____	G _____
B _____	N _____

41

M: What 'M' is loose earth, a woolly growth and a templet?

O: What 'O' is very fine translucent muslin?

K: What 'K' is a South African elevated plateau?

D: What 'D' is a wood nymph?

J: What 'J' is a hard oriental varnish?

P: What 'P' is partly blind?

H: What 'H' is a hollow place in a solid body?

W: What 'W' is the capital of the USA?

F: What 'F' comes before gate, light and water?

B: What 'B' is between salt and fresh water?

L: What 'L' means to flop about or move in an ungainly way?

S: What 'S' is the currency of Israel?

T: What 'T' is a picture or carving on three panels side by side?

R: What 'R' is an actor's part?

C: What 'C' beat cancer to win the 1981 Grand National?

E: What 'E' is a female sheep?

A: What 'A' is a river – and a warrior woman?

V: What 'V' is robust energy that goes with vigour?

G: What 'G' is a wreath of flowers?

N: What 'N' is a recent arrival?

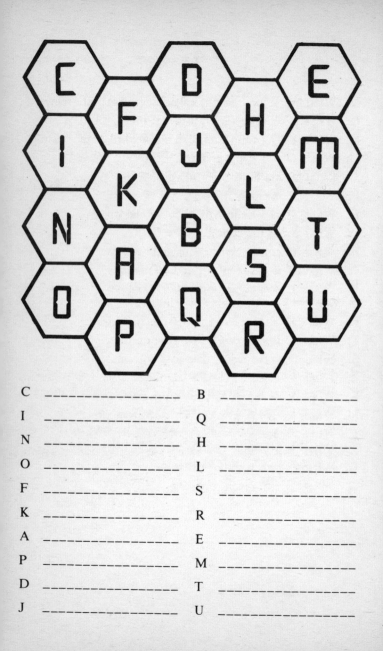

C _____
I _____
N _____
O _____
F _____
K _____
A _____
P _____
D _____
J _____

B _____
Q _____
H _____
L _____
S _____
R _____
E _____
M _____
T _____
U _____

42

C: What 'C' is the internal diameter of a gun?

I: What 'I' comes before gotten, omened and natured?

N: What 'N' is to indent – and catch a criminal?

O: What 'O' is a body of instrumental performers?

F: What 'F' is a limb adapted for swimming?

K: What 'K' is the green Alpine New Zealand parrot?

A: What 'A' is a violent poison?

P: What 'P' is a colour of mixed red and blue?

D: What 'D' comes after evening, morning and full?

J: What 'J' is a breed of cattle, jumper and island?

B: What 'B' is a plump and comely woman?

Q: What 'Q' means most essential or typical?

H: What 'H' is aimless?

L: What 'L' is money – and a sweet on a stick?

S: What 'S' is the upper part of a loin of beef?

R: What 'R' is a tiny thrush with an orange-red throat?

E: What 'E' comes before day, one and body?

M: What 'M' is a nocturnal, lepidopterous insect?

T: What 'T' is a soft felt hat with indented crown?

U: What 'U' is the capital of the Mongolian People's Republic?

G _____	I _____
Y _____	L _____
A _____	P _____
T _____	O _____
V _____	H _____
S _____	F _____
U _____	D _____
B _____	M _____
E _____	J _____
N _____	R _____

43

G: What 'G' is spirited – and lame or crippled?

Y: What 'Y' is a veil worn by Moslem women?

A: What 'A' is a missile shot from a bow?

T: What 'T' is connected with a catch as a means of release?

V: What 'V' is a nest of wasps?

S: What 'S' comes before coach, manager and whisper?

U: What 'U' is a usually localised rebellion?

B: What 'B' is a fluid secreted by the liver?

E: What 'E' is according to the Christian Gospel?

N: What 'N' means lower?

I: What 'I' is one who poses as someone else?

L: What 'L' is a guiding star?

P: What 'P' is the fleshy part of fruit?

O: What 'O' is a musician's composition?

H: What 'H' is a family's dwelling place?

F: What 'F' is a switchblade?

D: What 'D' is fine, dense drops of rain?

M: What 'M' means of this world?

J: What 'J' was a patient biblical patriarch?

R: What 'R' is a humanoid machine?

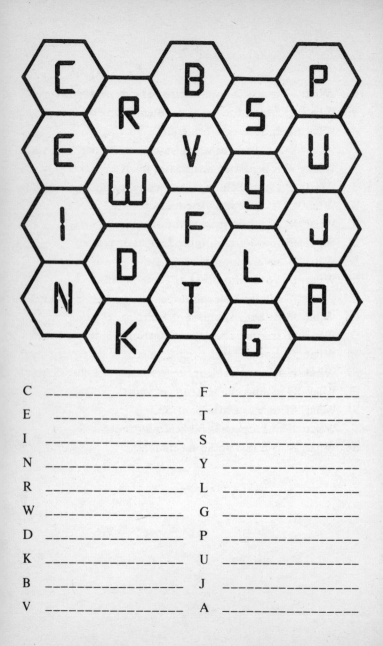

C _____   F _____

E _____   T _____

I _____   S _____

N _____   Y _____

R _____   L _____

W _____   G _____

D _____   P _____

K _____   U _____

B _____   J _____

V _____   A _____

44

C: What 'C' is a ruler and the successors of Mohammed?

E: What 'E' is the science of producing fine offspring?

I: What 'I' is a wild Alpine goat?

N: What 'N' is the Greek goddess of retribution?

R: What 'R' comes before coaster, blind and skate?

W: What 'W' is martial?

D: What 'D' is silly nonsense or twaddle?

K: What 'K' is a dust-coloured dull yellow?

B: What 'B' is a burning log – and trade mark?

V: What 'V' is prolix or overwordy?

F: What 'F' is to strip off skin?

T: What 'T' is a three-pronged spear – and a guided missile?

S: What 'S' is a division of a poem?

Y: What 'Y' is an archaic form of the definitive article?

L: What 'L' is the meeting place of a fraternal organisation?

G: What 'G' is a shrub with large white or yellow flowers?

P: What 'P' is to steal?

U: What 'U' is unreasonable or inopportune?

J: What 'J' is a crowbar favoured by burglars?

A: What 'A' was a Greek god who held up the world?

F _____	N _____
O _____	J _____
K _____	S _____
R _____	H _____
T _____	U _____
A _____	G _____
E _____	M _____
B _____	W _____
P _____	C _____
D _____	L _____

45

F: What 'F' comes before back, length and house?

O: What 'O' is a dramatic performance of which music is an essential part?

K: What 'K' is an Israeli collective farm?

R: What 'R' is a horse that's bay or chestnut mixed with white?

T: What 'T' is a trifling ornament?

A: What 'A' is a gas used as a filler for light bulbs?

E: What 'E' means to flow back?

B: What 'B' means like an arm?

P: What 'P' is a curtain to screen certain women from strangers?

D: What 'D' is a small draught of spirit?

N: What 'N' is late Stone Age?

J: What 'J' is a triangular sail, or projecting arm of a crane?

S: What 'S' is bacon with lines of fat and lean?

H: What 'H' foreshadows what is to come?

U: What 'U' comes before Jack and after trade?

G: What 'G' are troops stationed defensively in a fortress?

M: What 'M' is to assault with intent to rob?

W: What 'W' is a unit of power?

C: What 'C' is a small mountain antelope?

L: What 'L' is a vein of metal ore?

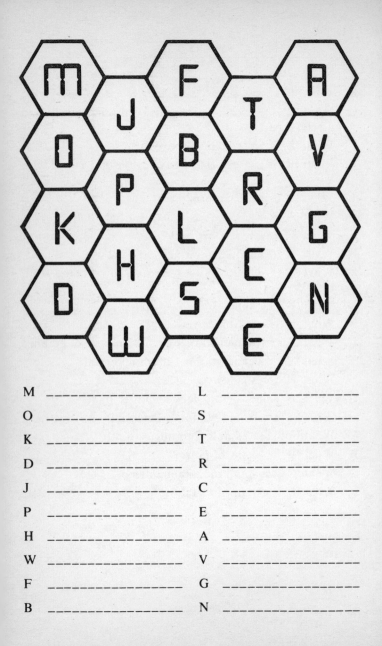

M _____

O _____

K _____

D _____

J _____

P _____

H _____

W _____

F _____

B _____

L _____

S _____

T _____

R _____

C _____

E _____

A _____

V _____

G _____

N _____

46

M: What 'M' is a building temporarily housing dead bodies?

O: What 'O' is a kind of quartz allied to agate?

K: What 'K' comes before fisher, maker and pin?

D: What 'D' is a Greek coin?

J: What 'J' is a counter with stamped or engraved motif?

P: What 'P' is a place of spiritual purging in the after life?

H: What 'H' is the official report of Parliamentary proceedings?

W: What 'W' is something designed to inflict bodily harm?

F: What 'F' is a time devoted to self-indulgence – or a casual attempt?

B: What 'B' is a clasp, suspending stays, and a pair?

L: What 'L' is a sign representing a word in shorthand?

S: What 'S' is to remove clothing?

T: What 'T' is to flow in a thin slow stream?

R: What 'R' is a bolt or pin that unites two metal plates?

C: What 'C' is to stop up a ship's seams with pitch?

E: What 'E' is the substitution of a mild expression for a harsh one?

A: What 'A' is an act of heinous wickedness?

V: What 'V' is a small ornamental bottle – and salad dressing?

G: What 'G' is an off-break ball bowled with leg-break action?

N: What 'N' is a tropical seabird – and a simpleton?

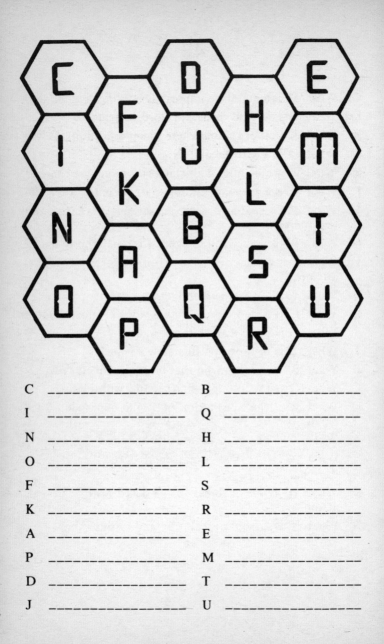

C _____
I _____
N _____
O _____
F _____
K _____
A _____
P _____
D _____
J _____

B _____
Q _____
H _____
L _____
S _____
R _____
E _____
M _____
T _____
U _____

47

C: What 'C' comes before kin, call and sup?

I: What 'I' means of Spain and Portugal?

N: What 'N' first propounded the theory of gravitation?

O: What 'O' is a kind of wild ass?

F: What 'F' means generating gas in the alimentary canal?

K: What 'K' is a Scottish church?

A: What 'A' is a perennial plant whose shoots are a delicacy?

P: What 'P' is a chrysalis?

D: What 'D' is a drawing of money by written order?

J: What 'J' is an opaque variety of quartz?

B: What 'B' is a blackberry shrub?

Q: What 'Q' is a member of the Society of Friends?

H: What 'H' is Japanese ritual suicide?

L: What 'L' is an anti-chamber, a bit of hair, and a fastener?

S: What 'S' is to machine gun from a low-flying aircraft?

R: What 'R' is your competitor?

E: What 'E' is to give off bubbles of gas?

M: What 'M' is the god of sleep or dreams?

T: What 'T' is a journey by ox wagon?

U: What 'U' means undertaken by one side only?

G _____	I _____
Y _____	L _____
A _____	P _____
T _____	O _____
V _____	H _____
S _____	F _____
U _____	D _____
B _____	M _____
E _____	J _____
N _____	R _____

48

G: What 'G' is a Hungarian stew?

Y: What 'Y' is a hard, low-growing evergreen tree?

A: What 'A' is a specialised slang?

T: What 'T' is to drag a net for fish?

V: What 'V' is the sixth zodiacal sign?

S: What 'S' is strong and fat – and a sweet, dark beer?

U: What 'U' comes before root, braid and stream?

B: What 'B' is a biro?

E: What 'E' is the interrelationship of life forms and the environments?

N: What 'N' means reduced to hopeless perplexity?

I: What 'I' means powerless or lacking in vigour?

L: What 'L' is to try to influence members of a legislate?

P: What 'P' is food boiled to pulp and liquidised?

O: What 'O' is the name of the Greek letter O?

H: What 'H' is grey haired with age?

F: What 'F' is a sudden transitory blaze?

D: What 'D' is two cards only of a suit?

M: What 'M' is a bog or marsh?

J: What 'J' is a kind of orange?

R: What 'R' is the prescribed way of performing a religious service?

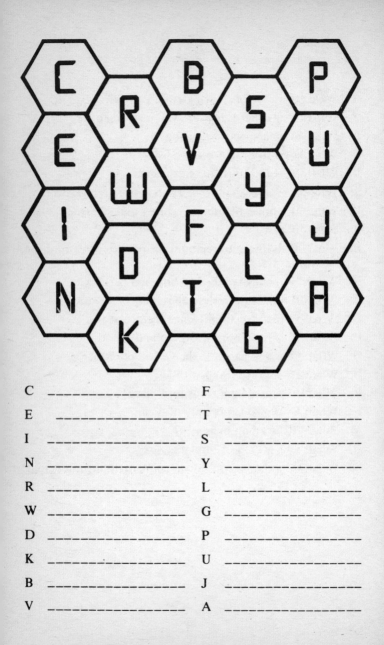

C _____
E _____
I _____
N _____
R _____
W _____
D _____
K _____
B _____
V _____

F _____
T _____
S _____
Y _____
L _____
G _____
P _____
U _____
J _____
A _____

49

C: What 'C' is a swivel-eyed, colour-changing lizard?

E: What 'E' means former?

I: What 'I' is ignorant of letters?

N: What 'N' is a female goat?

R: What 'R' is a mass of fish eggs?

W: What 'W' comes before cock, louse and pecker?

D: What 'D' is a plug of tobacco left unsmoked in a pipe?

K: What 'K' means blood relationship?

B: What 'B' is an ale cask, the thicker end – and a shooter's stand?

V: What 'V' means of the nature of vice?

F: What 'F' is hair that is a pale yellowish-brown?

T: What 'T' is a trembling effect in singing?

S: What 'S' comes after tomb, gall and hail?

Y: What 'Y' is a semi-solid preparation of fermented milk?

L: What 'L' is disinclined or reluctant?

G: What 'G' is a connoisseur of food and wine?

P: What 'P' is feeble, weak and undersized?

U: What 'U' is one prepared to act another's part?

J: What 'J' is a West Indian republic?

A: What 'A' is a thistle-like plant with an edible flower head?

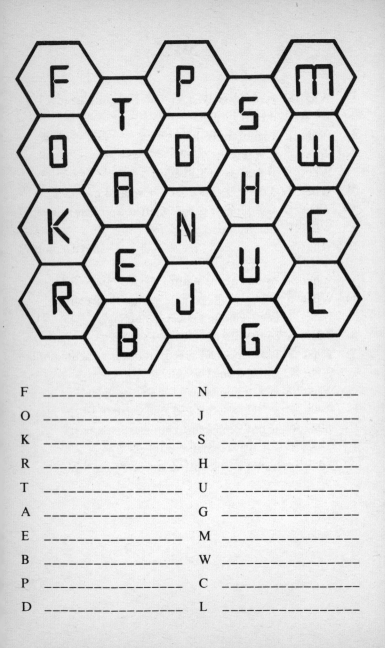

F _____ N _____

O _____ J _____

K _____ S _____

R _____ H _____

T _____ U _____

A _____ G _____

E _____ M _____

B _____ W _____

P _____ C _____

D _____ L _____

50

F: What 'F' is a small cake of syrup and oats?

O: What 'O' is the mountain where the Greek gods lived?

K: What 'K' is an unprincipled fellow or rogue?

R: What 'R' is a violent public disorder?

T: What 'T' is the main tube by which air passes to the lungs?

A: What 'A' is a fancy flat race meeting?

E: What 'E' is a negatively charged elementary atomic particle?

B: What 'B' comes before storm, pan and wave?

P: What 'P' is a small figure moved by strings?

D: What 'D' is doctrine laid down by the Church?

N: What 'N' are plants with stinging hairs?

J: What 'J' is a place of ruthless struggle for survival?

S: What 'S' means mean?

H: What 'H' are jointed devices on a door?

U: What 'U' means ingratiatingly smooth?

G: What 'G' means article of clothing?

M: What 'M' is a machine gun – and general truth?

W: What 'W' is to attack from ambush?

C: What 'C' is a Swiss mountain cottage?

L: What 'L' is fertile soil chiefly of clay and sand?

M _____	L _____
O _____	S _____
K _____	T _____
D _____	R _____
J _____	C _____
P _____	E _____
H _____	A _____
W _____	V _____
F _____	G _____
B _____	N _____

51

M: What 'M' is an alcoholic drink made from honey?

O: What 'O' is best or most favourable?

K: What 'K' is a cumin-flavoured liqueur?

D: What 'D' comes before trodden, right and hearted?

J: What 'J' is matter thrown overboard to lighten a ship in distress?

P: What 'P' is a learned man or teacher?

H: What 'H' is a chronological record of past events?

W: What 'W' is a place where rabbits abound?

F: What 'F' is a flourish of trumpets?

B: What 'B' is imitation butter?

L: What 'L' is a glandular organ that purifies the blood?

S: What 'S' is to dissipate or spend wastefully?

T: What 'T' is a rising body of warm air?

R: What 'R' is an Italian dish of rice and chicken?

C: What 'C' is the eastern part of a church reserved for clergy?

E: What 'E' is the congress of Welsh bards?

A: What 'A' is an East African soldier or guard?

V: What 'V' is an animal with a spinal column?

G: What 'G' is a round, Dutch cheese?

N: What 'N' is undue favour shown to relatives?

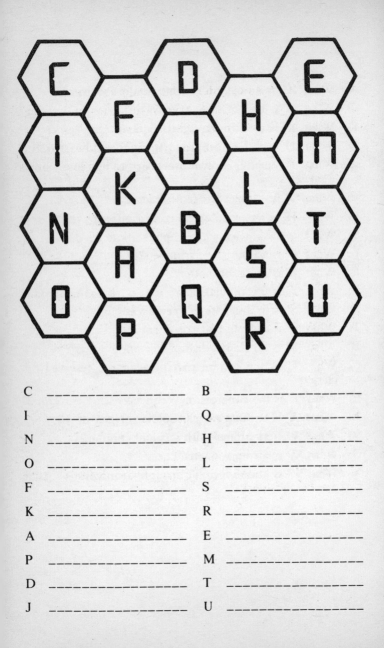

C _____	B _____
I _____	Q _____
N _____	H _____
O _____	L _____
F _____	S _____
K _____	R _____
A _____	E _____
P _____	M _____
D _____	T _____
J _____	U _____

52

C: What 'C' is a Scottish two-handed broadsword?

I: What 'I' is a tapering formation produced by freezing?

N: What 'N' is the Buddhist paradise?

O: What 'O' is the 24th and last letter of the Greek alphabet?

F: What 'F' is a trying predicament, a position found and a junkie's shot?

K: What 'K' is a bag strapped to the back?

A: What 'A' is any microbe that lives on free oxygen from the air?

P: What 'P' is to reduce to powder?

D: What 'D' is scurf?

J: What 'J' is a court entertainer?

B: What 'B' comes before window, man and line?

Q: What 'Q' is a traitor who collaborates with invaders?

H: What 'H' is a humorous or mischievous deception?

L: What 'L' is America's best known statue?

S: What 'S' is another word for a docker?

R: What 'R' is a small fried cake of cooked, minced food?

E: What 'E' is to supplement, contrive to make?

M: What 'M' is a lively Polish dance?

T: What 'T' means poisonous?

U: What 'U' is an avant-garde group that functions outside the Establishment?

G _____	I _____
Y _____	L _____
A _____	P _____
T _____	O _____
V _____	H _____
S _____	F _____
U _____	D _____
B _____	M _____
E _____	J _____
N _____	R _____

53

G: What 'G' is a large, short-winged hawk?

Y: What 'Y' is a bridge hand with no card above a nine?

A: What 'A' is a slender Zulu spear?

T: What 'T' is a perennial plant with a single woody stem?

V: What 'V' is a service of evening worship?

S: What 'S' is an instrument to study sounds in our bodies?

U: What 'U' is a university student who has not taken his degree?

B: What 'B' means sham?

E: What 'E' is senior – and a white flowered tree?

N: What 'N' is a woman's Wimbledon champion?

I: What 'I' is the striking of one thing against another?

L: What 'L' comes before bow, hand and jump?

P: What 'P' is observant of the appointed time?

O: What 'O' can't you make without breaking eggs?

H: What 'H' is a trough on a pole for carrying mortar?

F: What 'F' is a light fleecy tuft?

D: What 'D' is a very dear person?

M: What 'M' is a woman's name that means song thrush?

J: What 'J' is a close-fitting sleeveless jacket?

R: What 'R' is a worthless horse, a split – and a stretch of broken water?

| Hexagon grid containing letters: C B P R S E V U W Y I F J D L N T G K A |

C _____ F _____

E _____ T _____

I _____ S _____

N _____ Y _____

R _____ L _____

W _____ G _____

D _____ P _____

K _____ U _____

B _____ J _____

V _____ A _____

54

C: What 'C' is cement mixed with sand and gravel?

E: What 'E' is a pachyderm?

I: What 'I' is an imbecile?

N: What 'N' is the upright post round which a spiral staircase winds?

R: What 'R' is a swift return thrust in fencing?

W: What 'W' comes before hope, house and elephant?

D: What 'D' is hazardous?

K: What 'K' is the Queen's famous diamond?

B: What 'B' is a French sweet?

V: What 'V' is a structure of arches that carries a road?

F: What 'F' is a stone slab, coarse grass and cloth used as a symbol?

T: What 'T' is a flat Mexican maize cake?

S: What 'S' is someone who breeds livestock?

Y: What 'Y' comes after tax, calendar and leap?

L: What 'L' is a society of marine underwriters?

G: What 'G' was a snake-haired woman whose look turned people to stone?

P: What 'P' is another word for cougar?

U: What 'U' is a tunnel taking one road beneath another?

J: What 'J' is to make a harsh, discordant noise?

A: What 'A' is a mythical being with 100 eyes?

F _____ N _____

O _____ J _____

K _____ S _____

R _____ H _____

T _____ U _____

A _____ G _____

E _____ M _____

B _____ W _____

P _____ C _____

D _____ L _____

55

F: What 'F' is to make a hissing or spluttering sound?

O: What 'O' are words whose sound suggests their meaning?

K: What 'K' is a rare inert gaseous element?

R: What 'R' means stiff or unyielding?

T: What 'T' is to touch so as to cause laughter?

A: What 'A' were the horses who sailed to find the Golden Fleece?

E: What 'E' is to preserve a body from decay?

B: What 'B' is a downy beetle – and the hum of a bee?

P: What 'P' is a draught horse, a drink, a puppet and a blow?

D: What 'D' is the stroke of a pen, a sudden burst and a unit of Morse?

N: What 'N' is the feeling you are going to be sick?

J: What 'J' is a young kangaroo?

S: What 'S' is a D-shaped metal frame suspended from a saddle?

H: What 'H' is a London park?

U: What 'U' is everywhere or omnipotent?

G: What 'G' comes before bladder, fly and stone?

M: What 'M' is a cocktail made with gin and dry vermouth?

W: What 'W' is pottery with a cameo-like design in white relief?

C: What 'C' comes before gang, mail and saw?

L: What 'L' is flexible or supple?

Solution: Puzzle 1

M: Mickle (or Mackle); O: Obscure; K: Kraal; D: Duress; J: Joule; P: Puff; H: Hassle; W: Woden; F: Finns; B: Bald; L: Lubricant; S: Swallow (or Swift); T: Tumble; R: Rue; C: Can; E: Eton; A: Avast; V: Vitamin; G: Grotto; N: National.

Solution: Puzzle 2

C: Cute; I: Inspection; N: Noctule; O: Octet; F: Furious; K: Kiss; A: Amicable (or Amiable); P: Pullet; D: Dust; J: Jaw; B: Bat; Q: Quince; H: Haunt; L: Lullaby; S: Squash; R: Raffles; E: Exalt; M: Mallard; T: Tycoon; U: Uniform.

Solution: Puzzle 3

G: Goitre; Y: Yule; A: Afghanistan; T: Turner; V: Vegetable; S: Swank; U: Universe; B: Burroughs; E: Eye; N: Nurd; I: Impoverish; L: Lager; P: Puck; O: Oral; H: Hype; F: False; D: Duplicity; M: Magnitude; J: John; R: Rafter.

Solution: Puzzle 4

C: Callaghan; E: Endeavour; I: Iceland; N: Nitric; R: Road; W: Wenceslas; D: Duodenum; K: Kite; B: Beetroot; V: Voyager; F: Fiend; T: Twinkle; S: Synonym; Y: Yesterday; L: Late; G: Grotesque; P: Psalm; U: Ungulate; J: Jerkin; A: Alexander (the Great).

Solution: Puzzle 5

F: Fire; O: Obdurate (or Obstinate); K: Kaisers; R: Rude; T: Turpentine; A: Alabama; E: Elbow; B: Batman; P: Paternal; D: Dungeon; N: Neuter; J: Judo; S: Swede; H: Horse; U: Unisex; G: Gaiter; M: Morning; W: Waterloo; C: Cruciform; L: Lament.

Solution: Puzzle 6

M: Mycology; O: Out; K: Kenya; D: Dulse; J: Jeroboam; P: Petrify; H: Hyperbole; W: Werewolf; F: Friendly; B: Beat; L: Liturgy; S: Squirm; T: Tungsten; R: Rod; C: Cuddle; E: Equate; A: Andalusia; V: Victoria; G: Guitar; N: Nippon.

Solution: Puzzle 7

C: Cruzeiro; I: Intimate; N: Nook; O: Offal; F: Ferreous; K: Klaxon; A: Andover; P: Perfidious; D: Dark; J: Jive; B: Behave; Q: Qualm; H: Hyper; L: Luck; S: Swerve; R: Rat; E: Elegant; M: Mermaid; T: Tundra; U: Udders.

Solution: Puzzle 8

G: Ghost; Y: Yo-yo; A: Andrew; T: True; V: Volga; S: Synod; U: Upon; B: Brother; E: End; N: Nazi; I: Iago; L: Lazy; P: Pine; O: Ozone; H: Hither; F: Freak; D: Dingo; M: Mask; J: Jove; R: Rowdy.

Solution: Puzzle 9

C: Chad; E: Etcetera; I: Itch; N: Noggin; R: Rattle; W: Warlock; D: Duralumin; K: Knickers; B: Buoyant; V: Verdict; F: Furtive; T: Tom; S: Syntax; Y: Yaw; L: Lobster; G: Generalissimo; P: Pride; U: Utmost; J: Juliet; A: Autopsy.

Solution: Puzzle 10

F: Fast; O: Ovoid; K: Kiln; R: Rachmaninov; T: Turn; A: Always; E: Eden; B: Booze; P: Paean; D: Dunlin; N: No-man's-land; J: Ju-ju; S: Synopsis; H: Hint; U: Utilise; G: Gemma; M: Mane; W: Wehrmacht; C: Candlemas; L: Letters.

Solution: Puzzle 11

M: Mount; O: Ophelia; K: Kitty; D: Dunce; J: Jumbo; P: Pop; H: Haunch; W: Wrinkle; F: Fancy; B: Berne; L: Lucifer; S: Syrup; T: Torture; R: Rays; C: Climax; E: Enterprise; A: Alleviate; V: Venus; G: Gemini; N: Nylon.

Solution: Puzzle 12

C: Call; I: Inverse; N: Nut; O: Outset; F: Furnace; K: Kip; A: Allow; P: Pride; D: Doxy; J: Jeans; B: Buddy; Q: Quoit; H: Horatio; L: Louvre; S: Synthesis; R: Rustic; E: Errant; M: Mudskipper; T: Tory; U: Usual.

Solution: Puzzle 13

G: Gelding; Y: Yokel; A: Ali; T: Two; V: Voluptuous; S: Syncronise; U: Uterus; B: Bang; E: Erse; N: Nuzzle; I: Invoice; L: Lambast; P: Porcine; O: Oxygen; H: Horace; F: Futile; D: Date; M: Mickey (or Minnie); J: Jagger; R: Rollick.

Solution: Puzzle 14

C: Carter; E: Espousal; I: Inveterate; N: Numbskull; R: Rough; W: Wrath; D: Dray; K: Kink; B: Bongo; V: Vaughan-Williams; F: Futtock; T: Teeth; S: Sylph; Y: Yodel; L: Luger; G: Genuflect; P: Present; U: Usurper; J: Jewel; A: Amin.

Solution: Puzzle 15

F: Franco; O: Outlaw; K: Knackered; R: Rosette; T: Tsigane; A: Arch; E: Esquire; B: Brutus; P: Peroxide; D: Drogue; N: Nugget; J: Jilt; S: Synagogue; H: Harry; U: Usher (or Usherette); G: Gentry; M: Mallet; W: Woolsack; C: Convoluted; L: Lynx.

Solution: Puzzle 16

M: Madonna; O: Ounce; K: Kleptomania; D: Denmark; J: Jeer; P: Proletariat; H: High; W: Wapiti; F: Forsyth; B: Babble; L: Lychee; S: Swoon; T: Trews; R: Rust; C: Contortionist; E: Eternal; A: Axle; V: Vulnerable; G: Genie; N: Nom-de-plume.

Solution: Puzzle 17

C: Cartoon; I: Invent; N: Noun; O: Ottoman; F: Fuzz; K: Kloof; A: Azure; P: Puppy; D: Drake; J: Juice; B: Bilious; Q: Quite; H: Hovercraft; L: Lynching; S: Swap; R: Rustle; E: Eurocrat; M: McGuigan; T: Tyrant; U: Ursine.

Solution: Puzzle 18

G: Genet; Y: Yap; A: Awl; T: Twin; V: Vivaldi; S: Sycamore; U: Urban; B: Burlap; E: Extra; N: Nous; I: Intoxication (or Inebriation); L: Lymph; P: Presley; O: Ostracise; H: Hoover; F: Flamenco; D: Drone; M: Mitterand; J: Jut; R: Ruth.

Solution: Puzzle 19

C: Chafe; E: Euthanasia; I: Italy; N: Novocaine; R: Rusk; W: Wing; D: Dyak; K: Kipper; B: Bonce; V: Vulpine; F: Flamingo; T: Turban; S: Sword; Y: Yankee; L: Lush; G: Geneva; P: Pernickety; U: Uproar; J: Just; A: Avuncular.

Solution: Puzzle 20

F: Flabby; O: Ouch (or Ow!); K: Knickerbockers; R: Ruse; T: Tweezers; A: Avian; E: Euphonious; B: Biochemistry; P: Pagoda; D: Dyspepsia; N: News; J: Jury; S: Swot; H: Huge; U: Upholster; G: Ghana (or Galon); M: Marcos; W: Whoa!; C: Chorus; L: Lurk.

Solution: Puzzle 21

M: Major; O: Ostensible; K: Knoll; D: Desdemona; J: Jump; P: Prolix; H: Higgins; W: Whig; F: Faustus (or Faust); B: Bucolic; L: Lurcher; S: Switch; T: Tutti-frutti; R: Runt; C: Christ; E: Eulogy; A: Avocado; V: Vulcan; G: Germane; N: Notre Dame.

Solution: Puzzle 22

C: Chirp; I: Improve; N: Nepal; O: Osprey; F: Fandango; K: Knot; A: Awry; P: Patrol; D: Donald (or Daffy); J: Junta; B: Benign; Q: Quaint; H: Hare; L: Lumbago; S: Swipe; R: Rupee; E: Exclaim; M: Musket; T: Turkey; U: Unguent.

Solution: Puzzle 23

G: Greece; Y: Yam; A: Averse; T: Turbine; V: Vow; S: Symbiosis; U: Ululate; B: Basic; E: Elf; N: Non; I: Israel; L: Lug; P: Patriot; O: Over; H: Hamlet; F: Future; D: Duvet; M: Moussaka; J: Journal; R: Rotterdam.

Solution: Puzzle 24

C: Cucumber; E: Elysium; I: Impress; N: Narcotic; R: Romania; W: Whey; D: Disney; K: Krona; B: Brucellosis; V: Vortex; F: Furze; T: Tarantula; S: Sabre; Y: Yeats; L: Low; G: Germ; P: Patina; U: Underwriter; J: Joss; A: Aurora.

Solution: Puzzle 25

F: Furlong; O: Osteopathy; K: Knobble; R: Rugby (or Rugger); T: Turmeric; A: Aurilave; E: Emanate; B: Bends; P: Patois; D: Durable; N: Noodle; J: Jonah; S: Shakespeare; H: Hiccup; U: Uncle Sam; G: Ginger; M: Myopic; W: Wren; C: Calvados; L: Lucre.

Solution: Puzzle 26

M: Minah (or Mina); O: Oscar; K: Kodiak; D: Desert; J: Juvenile; P: Prow; H: Helicopter; W: Whelk; F: Flame; B: Baron; L: Low; S: Salad; T: Tumour; R: Rubble; C: Centigrade; E: Elba; A: Auto; V: Vodka; G: Gherkin; N: Nondescript.

Solution: Puzzle 27

C: Crufts; I: Imports; N: Nonagenarian; O: Oryx; F: Furl; K: Kurd; A: Aura; P: Pungent; D: Dynamo; J: Jute; B: Balloon; Q: Queer; H: Henchman; L: Latex; S: Saké; R: Ruminant; E: Everglades; M: Mud; T: Tuition; U: U-boat.

Solution: Puzzle 28

G: Ghee; Y: Yemen; A: Ambivalent; T: Tulip; V: Void; S: Salami; U: UHF; B: Bug; E: Easter; N: Nonentity; I: Impetus; L: Lasagne; P: Pekinese; O: Orphan; H: Hunch; F: Fiscal; D: Dormer; M: Mute; J: Jenny; R: Rhine.

Solution: Puzzle 29

C: Carbon; E: Effete; I: Implant; N: Nominal; R: Ruby; W: Wharf; D: Dorsal; K: Kudos; B: Budd; V: Viviparous; F: Fitch; T: Tug; S: Swelter; Y: Yugoslavia; L: Lava; G: Giant; P: Pell-mell; U: Unclean; J: Justice; A: Authentic.

Solution: Puzzle 30

F: Fish; O: Oscillate; K: Krass; R: Rosemary; T: Tripod; A: Autocracy; E: Extrovert; B: Bugle; P: Pelucid; D: Doodle; N: Nostradamus; J: Juxtapose; S: Swami; H: Haversack; U: Undulant; G: Gibberish; M: Mussel; W: Work; C: Chow Mein; L: Lorn.

Solution: Puzzle 31

M: MOT; O: Open; K: Kale; D: Dumdum; J: Jura; P: Pulse; H: Hirohito;
W: Weed; F: Finite; B: Bats; L: Lotion; S: Swag; T: Truss; R: Royal;
C: Concorde; E: Exuberant; A: Augur; V: Vlad (the Impaler); G: Gingham;
N: Nimbus.

Solution: Puzzle 32

C: Candle; I: Incognito; N: Non; O: Ostler; F: Flan; K: Kowtow; A: Adore;
P: Pelmet; D: Dollop; J: Juniper; B: Brawn; Q: Quota; H: Helsinki; L: LP;
S: Surly; R: Rowan; E: Eyelet; M: Mucus; T: Truncheon; U: United.

Solution: Puzzle 33

G: Galoshes; Y: Yukon; A: Attorney; T: Trots; V: Vitriol; S: Sub;
U: Ullswater; B: Brown; E: Eyas; N: Nicker; I: Illusory; L: Lorikeet (or Lorg);
P: Pyrotechnics; O: Orbit; H: Haricot; F: Fives; D: Dub; M: Musquash;
J: Jukebox; R: Rouble.

Solution: Puzzle 34

C: Claudius; E: Exude; I: Immerse; N: Noyade; R: Rubber; W: Wensleydale;
D: Drunkard (or Dypsomaniac); K: Keep; B: Bully; V: Vitrify; F: Fungicide;
T: Trotter; S: Suitor; Y: Yacht; L: Love; G: Gallows (or Gibbet); P: Pyrex;
U: University; J: Junket; A: Aegis.

Solution: Puzzle 35

F: Fund; O: Ossuary; K: Karate; R: Rookie; T: Truffle; A: Ash Wednesday;
E: Extent; B: Bumf; P: Putt; D: Dog; N: Noxious (or Noisome); J: Jowl;
S: Sultan; H: Hind; U: UN; G: Gambit; M: Motor; W: Weasel; C: Climate;
L: Longjohns.

Solution: Puzzle 36

M: Must; O: Oodles; K: Kopek; D: Dock; J: Jiffy; P: Pyre; H: Hard;
W: Weave; F: Fug; B: Bonanza; L: Lord; S: Suet; T: Trucklebed;
R: Rookery; C: Canute; E: Extinct; A: Aeolian; V: Venice; G: Germicide;
N: Nip.

Solution: Puzzle 37

C: Chicken; I: Immediate; N: Nietzsche; O: Orchard; F: Fudge; K: Kayak; A: Aries; P: Push; D: Doldrums; J: Jeopardy; B: Beatles; Q: Quintuplets; H: Hydrofoil; L: Loquacious; S: Suffragette; R: Romany; E: Explode; M: Munch (or Masticate); T: Trotsky; U: Usk.

Solution: Puzzle 38

G: Gangrene; Y: Yellow-hammer; A: Arcady; T: Triumphant; V: Vocation; S: Super; U: Uttoxeter; B: Blockbusters; E: Expert; N: Nickel; I: Imbibe; L: Lope; P: Purse; O: Osmium; H: Harem; F: Flaw; D: Disraeli; M: Muscle; J: Jennet; R: Rowlock.

Solution: Puzzle 39

C: Columbus; E: Exhaust; I: Inter; N: Niche; R: Roquefort; W: Warp; D: Duct; K: Kaddish; B: Box; V: Vintage; F: Flea; T: Trowel; S: Suede; Y: Ypres; L: Lopsided; G: Gibbon; P: Puzzle; U: Unst; J: Jumper; A: Archer.

Solution: Puzzle 40

F: Frump; O: Oregano; K: Kalong; R: Roman; T: Tripe; A: Arbour; E: Eve; B: Butter; P: Puttee; D: Duce; N: New; J: Jaywalk; S: Sucrose; H: Henna; U: Utrecht; G: Gape; M: Muse; W: Wee; C: Carol; L: Loofah.

Solution: Puzzle 41

M: Mould; O: Organdie; K: Karroo; D: Dryad; J: Japan; P: Purblind; H: Hole; W: Washington; F: Flood; B: Brackish; L: Lollop; S: Shekel; T: Triptych; R: Role; C: Champion; E: Ewe; A: Amazon; V: Vim; G: Garland; N: Newcomer.

Solution: Puzzle 42

C: Calibre; I: Ill; N: Nick; O: Orchestra; F: Flipper; K: Kea; A: Arsenic; P: Purple; D: Dress; J: Jersey; B: Buxom; Q: Quintessential; H: Haphazard; L: Lolly; S: Sirloin; R: Robin; E: Every; M: Moth; T: Trilby; U: Ulan Bator.

Solution: Puzzle 43

G: Game; Y: Yashmak; A: Arrow; T: Trigger; V: Vespiary; S: Stage;
U: Uprising; B: Bile; E: Evangelic; N: Nether; I: Imposter; L: Lodestar;
P: Pulp; O: Opus; H: Home; F: Flick-knife; D: Drizzle; M: Mundane; J: Job;
R: Robot.

Solution: Puzzle 44

C: Caliph; E: Eugenics; I: Ibex; N: Nemesis; R: Roller; W: Warlike;
D: Drivel; K: Khaki; B: Brand; V: Verbose; F: Flay; T: Trident; S: Stanza;
Y: Ye; L: Lodge; G: Gardenia; P: Purloin (or Pinch); U: Untimely;
J: Jemmy; A: Atlas.

Solution: Puzzle 45

F: Full; O: Opera; K: Kibbutz; R: Roan; T: Trinket; A: Argon; E: Ebb;
B: Brachial; P: Purdah; D: Dram; N: Neolithic; J: Jib; S: Streaky;
H: Harbinger; U: Union; G: Garrison; M: Mug; W: Watt; C: Chamois;
L: Lode.

Solution: Puzzle 46

M: Mortuary (or Morgue); O: Onyx; K: King; D: Drachma; J: Jetton;
P: Purgatory; H: Hansard; W: Weapon; F: Fling; B: Brace; L: Logogram;
S: Strip; T: Trickle; R: Rivet; C: Caulk; E: Euphemism; A: Atrocity;
V: Vinaigrette; G: Googly; N: Noddy.

Solution: Puzzle 47

C: Cat; I: Iberian; N: Newton; O: Onager; F: Flatulant; K: Kirk;
A: Asparagus; P: Pupa; D: Draft; J: Jasper; B: Bramble; Q: Quaker;
H: Hara-kiri; L: Lock; S: Strafe; R: Rival; E: Effervesce; M: Morpheus;
T: Trek; U: Unilateral.

Solution: Puzzle 48

G: Goulash; Y: Yew; A: Argot; T: Trawl; V: Virgo; S: Stout; U: Up;
B: Ballpoint; E: Ecology; N: Nonplussed; I: Impotent; L: Lobby; P: Puree;
O: Omicron; H: Hoar; F: Flash; D: Doubleton; M: Morass; J: Jaffa;
R: Ritual.

Solution: Puzzle 49

C: Chameleon; E: Erstwhile; I: Illiterate; N: Nanny; R: Roe; W: Wood; D: Dottle; K: Kinship; B: Butt; V: Vicious; F: Flaxen; T: Tremolo; S: Stone; Y: Yoghourt; L: Loath; G: Gourmet; P: Puny; U: Understudy; J: Jamaica; A: Artichoke.

Solution: Puzzle 50

F: Flapjack; O: Olympus; K: Knave; R: Riot; T: Trachea; A: Ascot; E: Electron; B: Brain; P: Puppet; D: Dogma; N: Nettles; J: Jungle; S: Stingy; H: Hinges; U: Unctious; G: Garment; M: Maxim; W: Waylay; C: Chalet; L: Loam.

Solution: Puzzle 51

M: Mead; O: Optimum; K: Kummel; D: Down; J: Jetsam; P: Pundit; H: History; W: Warren; F: Fanfare; B: Butterine; L: Liver; S: Squander; T: Thermal; R: Risotto; C: Chancel; E: Eisteddfod; A: Askari; V: Vertebrate; G: Gouda; N: Nepotism.

Solution: Puzzle 52

C: Claymore; I: Icicle; N: Nirvana; O: Omega; F: Fix; K: Knapsack; A: Aerobe; P: Pulverise; D: Dandruff; J: Jester; B: Bow; Q: Quisling; H: Hoax; L: Liberty; S: Stevedore; R: Rissole; E: Eke; M: Mazurka; T: Toxic; U: Underground.

Solution: Puzzle 53

G: Goshawk; Y: Yarborough; A: Assagai; T: Tree; V: Vespers; S: Stethoscope; U: Undergraduate; B: Bogus; E: Elder; N: Navratilova; I: Impact; L: Long; P: Punctual; O: Omelette; H: Hod; F: Flake; D: Darling; M: Mavis; J: Jerkin; R: Rip.

Solution: Puzzle 54

C: Concrete; E: Elephant; I: Idiot; N: Newel; R: Riposte; W: White; D: Dangerous; K: Koh-i-noor; B: Bonbon; V: Viaduct; F: Flag; T: Tortilla; S: Stockbreeder; Y: Year; L: Lloyds; G: Gorgon; P: Puma; U: Underpass; J: Jangle; A: Argus.

Solution: Puzzle 55

F: Fizz; O: Onomatopoeia; K: Krypton; R: Rigid; T: Tickle; A: Argonauts;
E: Embalm; B: Buzz; P: Punch; D: Dash; N: Nausea; J: Joey; S: Stirrup;
H: Hyde; U: Ubiquitous; G: Gall; M: Martini; W: Wedgwood; C: Chain;
L: Lithe.

The Freakiest, Funniest Book About Animals – *Ever!*

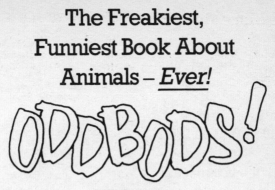

Bill Garnett

FIRST THERE WAS *THE NAKED APE*. THEN CAME *THE NAKED NUN*... NOW – AT LAST – THE NAKED TRUTH!

There are creatures that walk this planet which:

* *Bathe in acid*
* *Baffle Radar*
* *Turn into plants*
* *Do business – and have sex – without their heads*

You'll find them – and many others even stranger – in *ODDBODS!*

IT'S EVERYTHING YOU NEVER WANTED TO KNOW ABOUT ANIMALS – BUT WILL BE STAGGERED TO HEAR!

HUMOUR/NON-FICTION   0 7221 3809 1   £1.75

A selection of bestsellers from SPHERE

FICTION

STREET SONG	Emma Blair	£3.50 ☐
GOLDEN TRIPLE TIME	Zoe Garrison	£2.95 ☐
BEACHES	Iris Rainer Dart	£2.95 ☐
RAINBOW SOLDIERS	Walter Winward	£3.50 ☐
FAMILY ALBUM	Danielle Steel	£2.95 ☐

FILM AND TV TIE-IN

MONA LISA	John Luther Novak	£2.50 ☐
BLOCKBUSTERS GOLD RUN		£1.95 ☐
9½ WEEKS	Elizabeth McNeil	£1.95 ☐
BOON	Anthony Masters	£2.50 ☐
AUF WIEDERSEHEN PET 2	Fred Taylor	£2.75 ☐

NON-FICTION

BURTON: THE MAN BEHIND THE MYTH	Penny Junor	£2.95 ☐
THE DISAPPEARED	John Simpson & Jana Bennett	£4.95 ☐
THE LAST NAZI: THE LIFE AND TIMES OF JOSEPH MENGELE	Gerald Astor	£3.50 ☐
THE FALL OF SAIGON	David Butler	£3.95 ☐
LET'S FACE IT	Christine Piff	£2.50 ☐

All Sphere books are available at your local bookshop or newsagent, or can be ordered direct from the publisher. Just tick the titles you want and fill in the form below.

Name _____

Address _____

_____

Write to Sphere Books, Cash Sales Department, P.O. Box 11, Falmouth, Cornwall TR10 9EN.

Please enclose a cheque or postal order to the value of the cover price plus:

UK: 55p for the first book, 22p for the second book and 14p for each additional book ordered to a maximum charge of £1.75.

OVERSEAS: £1.00 for the first book plus 25p per copy for each additional book.

BFPO & EIRE: 55p for the first book, 22p for the second book plus 14p per copy for the next 7 books, thereafter 8p per book.

Sphere Books reserve the right to show new retail prices on covers which may differ from those previously advertised in the text or elsewhere, and to increase postal rates in accordance with the PO.